About the Authors

We are the two Fannies, two middle aged women who came together as friends, brought together by our crazy personal and professional experiences.

We consider ourselves soul fannies, because of the similarities we have experienced in our lives.

We have both been bullied, and it affected our lives on a physical, emotional and spiritual level.

We have also both been in relationships with abusive narcissists, being lucky enough to have survived those crazy bastards.

Writing our book has been a source of profound healing and has bought happiness back into our lives.

We hope that our book enables the reader to find the same hap-penis.

The Tales of Two Fannies

Fanny and Fanny

The Tales of Two Fannies

Olympia Publishers
London

www.olympiapublishers.com
OLYMPIA PAPERBACK EDITION

A CIP catalogue record for this title is
available from the British Library.

ISBN: 978-1-78830-747-5

This is a work of creative nonfiction. The events are portrayed to the
best of the author's memory. While all the stories in this book are
true, some names and identifying details have been changed to
protect the privacy of the people involved.

First Published in 2020

Olympia Publishers
Tallis House
2 Tallis Street
London
EC4Y 0AB

Printed in Great Britain

Dedication

Dedicated to our families.
We are sorry for any embarrassment we may have caused
you.
The legacy we leave you with this book, you will never ever
forget.
We love you all, and hope you enjoy the ride as much as we
did.
Love 'The Fannies'.

Acknowledgements

The Fannies would like to give a *Fanny high five* to all the incredible characters that grace the pages of their unique, no-holds-barred book. If they hadn't met you, screwed you, or been screwed over by you, they would never have been able to write about you.

Their book has coincided with the COVID-19 pandemic, and they would like the reader to know that while some of the characters are reflected in a negative light, this by no means represents the majority of healthcare workers – who provide compassionate care and commitment in the work they do within the health care industry.

To Fanny Two's dad, thank you for doing the proofreading. Fanny One thinks your mind is as dirty as hers.

To Lel, thank you for not really charging $10,000 in danger money to edit the book. The Fannies can barely afford a cheap bottle of Prosecco. Hopefully, their book will change this sad and sorry fact, and they may even be able to buy two!

To the Fannies' five children, okay, we get it... the Fannies have embarrassed you, but please bear in mind you ruined their once-skinny bodies... just get over it. When they pop their clogs you will be well looked after.

To all the narcissists who have crossed the Fannies' path; you actually had a purpose in their lives after all. They salute you and kiss your fungus-infested feet. Without your evil endeavours, their book would never have come to fruition. The Fannies sincerely hope that those reading wake up and smell the stench of your toxic piss, run as fast as they can, and never look back.

Finally, thanks to all of you who read the book on its trial run. Your feedback ensured the Fannies put their tales out there for all the world to see.

Let's fill up our flutes with Prosecco, never munch on a banana again, and toast the rollercoaster ride that is *The Two Fannies*.

Thank you for reading.

The Fannies' Mission Statement
'Sprinkling magic fairy dust around the universe, to create
hap-penis, and a more caring world.'

The Fannies Disclaimer

This is a work of non-fiction. The Fannies have re-created the events, locales, and conversations from their memories of their life events.

In order to maintain anonymity; names, characters, businesses, places, events, locals and incidents, including details such as physical properties, identifying characteristics, occupations and places of residence, have been changed to protect the parties involved. Any resemblance to any persons living or dead, is strictly coincidental.

The book is not intended as a substitute for the medical advice of a decent doctor. The reader should consult with a doctor or medical professional, with any and all matters relating to their health.

Although the Fannies and publisher have made every effort to ensure that the information in this book was correct at the time of press, the Fannies and publisher do not assume and hereby disclaim any liability to any party for loss, damage, or disruption caused by errors or omissions which may result in negligence, accident or any other cause.

So 'jog on' if you have a problem with this!

Introduction

Hold onto your 'fanny flaps' (or your shlong), as you are taken on the rollercoaster ride of your life. The Fannies invite you to take a peek through their Fanny curtains, into their secret world of mishaps and mayhem.

It just can't be true! You will say to yourself, *but it must be, because the Fannies say it is.*

Well… it's all true, dear reader.

The Fannies have lived these tales, and promise they are one hundred percent factual. Only the names dates and places have been changed, to protect the innocent parties.

Some of these tales might resonate with you, and you may even ask yourself: *Could the Fannies be talking about me…?*

Read it and weep!

The Fannies certainly did, while writing this book.

The two Fannies met when finding themselves employed in similar roles. Their connection was immediate. In their previous lives, they had both been nurses and had spent many years working in hospitals around the world. They then moved into a world they found unfamiliar and, at times, suffocating. The Fannies would often look up from their computers and roll their eyes at one another:

"How catatonic the corporate world has become, Fanny."

Their office is full of what they labelled 'The PC Robots.' Their boss sits in his ivory tower, in a suit two sizes too small for his weedy frame. They would like him to know this was a very bad decision and that the outline of his wiener left no lasting impression on either of them.

He is a sociopathic cannibal, who eats people alive. (The cannibalism here fits with a certain chapter of this book.) This narcissistic monster scaremongers people into submission, leaving them so broken, that they crawl back into their shell or leave.

He wants to be surrounded by 'yes' people, and the damage he does to those who question him with a 'no' is brutal. He starts them off with the 'silent treatment,' and then it gets worse.

Rumour has it, the psychopath then gets them into his office and threatens the 'no people' with defamatory accusations, until they leave. The ridiculous thing is this: he works in an area focused on the wellbeing of staff, and everyone is too intimidated to do anything to help their own.

The Fannies aren't scared; they have met people like this before.

Why? For a time, they each loved one, but that story is for another day. The Fannies wrote a letter to the biggest boss in their corporation, telling the truth, the whole truth, and nothing but the truth, just like this book.

As you read, you may experience a little exaggeration here and there but, pants on fire, they are no liars!

'Mr Psychopath' doesn't know it was they, who wrote the letter, unless he is reading this book now. Sitting alone, sucking off his teddy bear, he is only misunderstood after all.

When the Fannies could, they would escape to the office café to de-program themselves, and it was there they would inevitably start talking about the defining moments of their nursing careers. The 'Catatonics' would stare at them, enviously wondering what all the noise was about: it was called 'belly-splitting laughter'.

They often thought how even just one of their tales would shock their colleagues, so much so, they might loosen up and throw caution to the wind, allowing themselves to see a lighter side of life.

The Fannies feel that people today have become detached and disconnected. They feel that people are having a better relationship with their mobile phones and computers than they do with each other. They also feel that people find it easier to laugh at the expense of others, more so than to laugh at themselves.

***

So, what was the catalyst for the Fannies writing this book? Director Mark was.

Director Mark had just been appointed as top dog of the firm, and the Fannies felt an immediate connection with him.

He was an outstanding 'silver fox' specimen of a man, which made an enormous change from the red-faced, hypertensive beer guts they had often dealt with.

He stood strong in his sense of self and they could see that with each ex-policeman step he took, he did so with the utmost integrity.

A&E nurses were often in the firing line as much as the police, so a friendship between the two was natural.

So natural in fact, that one of the Fannies once found herself arrested, on her back, in the back of a police paddy wagon, in the centre of a busy London street. She said the policeman's helmet was a perfect fit.

Director Mark just happened to reside in the same town as one of the Fannies, many years before. Fanny asked him if he remembered a French-Canadian cop who was known as 'Dr Spock' by the hospital staff, and director Mark said he knew him well. Dr Spock had a thick French accent which matched his jet-black curly hair and bicycle-handle moustache. Fanny can't recall if he carried a string of onions around his neck.

Dr Spock often brought in those 'but I'm innocent, m'lord' types for treatment for their dog bites, it was commonplace back then to 'release the hounds', to catch those on the run. Those bitten were a sorry lot, and Fanny would offer her 'you silly bugger' compassion as they dropped their torn trousers for a complimentary tetanus shot.

(Not to be confused with the man who gets buggered later on in this book.)

On one particular occasion, Dr Spock arrived with a bedraggled young man who had been on the receiving end of a police dog's dinnertime canines.

As Fanny's patient required extensive repair work to his wounds, Dr Spock left her to get on with the job and he went off to have a chat with the real doctor, leaving his police radio sitting on the clinic trolley.

When Fanny completed her mighty fine work, she turned away briefly, only to feel something suddenly brush past her. She turned around and saw her patient taking his leave, while tucking the police radio into the back of his pants.

"Ooh la la! Ee eez escaping!" she exclaimed.

Dr Spock jumped up from his seat and proceeded to re-capture his escapee. He ran up behind him, reaching out and grabbing him by the scruff of his neck. Placing his Vulcan fingers firmly to the side of his neck, he then pinched and pressed firmly.

The man dropped to the floor like a sack of spuds.

Dr Spock then casually retrieved his radio from the back of the man's pants, stepped over him, and went back to continue his discussion with the doctor.

The staff continued attending to their patients, and the failed escapee was stepped over quite a few times before he woke up. When he did, he was even more bewildered than when he first came in. Dr Spock cuffed his prisoner and, as you would expect, he spoke the following words into his radio:

"Beam me up Scotty, sil vous plait."

They were both gone in a flash.

Mark mentioned that it was no longer permissible for the police to use the Vulcan technique. Such a shame, thought the Fannies, given its entertainment value.

The Fannies discussed many other 'back in the day' stories which led the conversation down the garden path to one particular tale, a tale that made headlines across the world.

"Did you hear about the elderly lady who came back to life in the morgue?" Fanny asked Mark.

She asked if he knew of the two new police recruits who had found her that day.

He leaned back in his chair and placed his hands behind his head and smirked, stating that he did know them.

Fanny told Mark that she had been one of the nurses on shift that day and that she had met the old dear when she was dead (well, almost!).

She then asked Mark if the two recruits had stayed in the job following the woman's resurrection and hoped they had received trauma counselling.

"No, we didn't have counselling Fanny, and yes, we both stayed in the job," smiled Mark.

The two Fannies then fell off their chairs and onto their fannies.

"We have to write a book!" They both said at the same time.

Fanny Fact:
Ethical Issues (aka We Don't Give a Shit)

Both Fannies have thought long and hard about the ethical issues that might come up in this book, and would like you to know they really don't give two fanny-fingered fucks!

No persons nor places have been identified and any coincidences are just that, nothing more than a coincidence. The Fannies have made every effort to protect the victims, and as much as they wanted to name and shame the perpetrators, they already know who they are.

They have to live with the karma of what they've done.

What is the Fanny Finger?

It is the Fannies' unique way of self- expression.

The Fannies hope you, too, will pick up this style of communication.

To explain it just a little further, if you are a woman, you will know exactly what it is.

It is the moment the doctor gloves-up, and lubes up, for his examination of your middle wind tunnel.

Do you need any further explanation, gentlemen?

Tale One:
Knocking on Heaven's Door, Well, Almost!

Once upon a time…

It was a bone chilling winter.

The city and its people felt like they were frozen to the bone, and unfortunately, some actually were.

Wrap yourself up please reader, since this is a chilling tale.

Back then, Fanny was living in an old and cold two-storey house in a rich street. The large sprawling house was owned by a geologist. He seemed a lonely man, and she thinks he rented out rooms for company.

A well-known name lived two doors down and she used to bike past, glancing up at the elaborate chandelier that hung in the entrance.

The geologist had a dog, and a girlfriend, whom he said was

'on again, off again'. The girlfriend, that is, not the dog!

Fanny and her roommates quickly came to the conclusion that it was mostly 'off', because they never actually met her.

The other thing that was off was his choice of vocation, as every three months, he would disappear into the mountains to illegally mine for gold, then he would return with dozens of buckets of black stony stash.

The weight of the buckets would kill his back lawn in patches, making it looking like it was covered in crop circles.

Once, when he was out looking for his girlfriend, Fanny and her roommates took turns to fish their hands deep inside the buckets in the hope of pulling out a gigantic golden nugget.

He told them he made enough to pay off his living expenses for months at a time, which gave him more time to sit and wait for his girlfriend to return.

No luck with the nuggets, by the way, or the girlfriend, for that matter.

He never once used any of his money to fix up his falling-down house. He had no energy, because sadly, he was falling down, too. He would spend hours staring at his fire as the wind screamed through the rotten seals on the window frames.

To keep warm that winter, the roommates felt it was easiest to stay in bed. The paper-thin walls made for entertaining listening and it was easy to tell which one of them had got lucky.

The landlord would often complain about the noise of their thrusting finales and the roommates hoped his broken heart would eventually mend, so he could have a finale of his own.

Fanny rode her bike through every season, and the ambulance staff would often give her a lift home during those winter months.

One of the senior doctors also kept offering her a different type of lift, onto his lap, he was kind of hot in a sleazy, middle-aged sort of way, and he had a penchant for young nurses.

The turn off for Fanny however, was his old-fashioned dress sense, his fat tie was as tired and out of date as his over-used fat member.

The biggest turn-off though, was his stalking of her. He would turn up on the oddest of occasions, jogging in the same park, or would just happen to be driving past.

Fanny was naturally oblivious of the fact that social media

was just around the corner, which would make things so much easier for stalkers.

The funny thing is, he used to be Fanny's granny's GP.

Her grandmother had a great giggle when Fanny told her that he had been caught having sex in one of the hospital cleaning cupboards, and Fanny said the floor mop was probably up his bum at the same time.

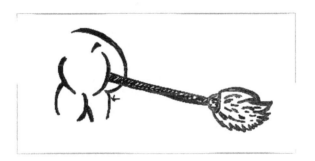

This particular year was a hypothermia-inducing winter, and they had got a call to say a patient was on her way in a frozen-to-the-bone state; she would arrive through the back entrance. The back entrance, as it was known, was where the duty doctor would view and certify the dead.

Fanny loved going to the back entrance. She was quite gory in that respect.

It was also common for the elderly to take to their beds during winter, but for different reasons than Fanny and her roommates. They did so out of necessity, because many couldn't afford the electricity to keep warm.

The ambulance staff had found the poor old dear on the floor beside her bed. They think she must have tried to get up to go to the bathroom and then slipped and fell. She was covered in excrement and they said they had to peel her frozen body off the wooden floor. It was clear she had lain there for days.

It broke Fanny's heart when they lifted the blankets. The old lady's wafer-thin nightgown barely covered her poverty-stricken frame. Plastic bread bags were tied up over her bed socks, as if to insulate her feet.

Fanny touched her and shivered.

They wheeled her into one of the clinic rooms, where Fanny added more blankets to keep her comfortable. Dead or not, Fanny thought she deserved some level of respect before being taken to the morgue.

The senior nurse then performed an ECG, while the doctor briefly looked at the results, and then looked back at her.

He said she was gone, and then he left.

To Fanny's mind, this was no sort of examination at all.

The hospital was busy, and the orderlies weren't able to take her straight to the morgue, after all, there wasn't any rush.

It was the end of Fanny's shift and for some reason, she decided to check in on her frozen patient one last time.

As Fanny looked down at her, she thought she saw

something from the corner of her eye, but due to tiredness, she thought her imagination was playing tricks.

Later that evening, in her freezing house, the phone rang.

Her nursing colleague was in an excited state, something about the A&E being the talk of the hospital, because of the cardiac arrest in the morgue.

Why, it even made the evening news!

The two fresh police recruits had probably never seen a dead body before, let alone a body that decided to come back to life. As they lifted her up to put her in the coroner's hearse, they heard a faint noise coming from beneath the zipper of the body bag.

"Is anyone there…?"

It was a miracle!

However, it was no bloody miracle at all, the old lady had been swaddled in Fanny's blankets and had simply warmed up while she was waiting to go to the morgue.

Fanny then recalled another 'back entrance' patient, but this one really was dead!

The police had found her in bed with the electric blanket on. They said she had started melting like an ice cream cone that had dropped onto a hot pavement.

Fanny had never seen a dead body quite that dead before, and my God, she couldn't wait.

"Are you ready Fanny?" asked the ambulance officer.

"Bring it on," she said.

"Are you sure you're ready for this?"

"Can't wait!"

Fanny hadn't noticed that the certifying doctor had stepped right back and was now partially hidden in the corner of the room.

"Come a bit closer so you can get a good look Fanny."

So, of course, she went closer, real close…

He slowly unzipped the body bag and Fanny's screams could be heard throughout the hospital, dozens of flies made their escape and buzzed around her excitedly, through her hair, up her nose, and into her mouth, Fanny thought she was their next victim.

"Do you think we can confirm her death, Miss Fanny Fly Blown?" the doctor laughed.

Now back to the frozen lady…

It wasn't flies waiting for her on the day she thawed out, it was a detective, wanting to discuss the 'not-quite-dead' body.

She was filling her knickers with worry, but not as much as the senior doctor and nurse. Fanny was their junior, and so who was she to speak up for herself? She was 'miss nobody' in the hospital rankings and was coached on what and what not to say.

"Yes, Mr Detective, she was absolutely dead! as dead as a…"

All through the interview, Fanny kept thinking about what she thought she had seen from the corner of her eye, but the doctor had certified her dead, so she must have been.

"It must have been a miracle," stammered Fanny, with her 'blue eyed innocent' look.

She thinks she may have even fluttered her eyelashes, because he was kind of hot, in a 'not-so-sleazy' kind of way.

Today, that certifying doctor is also dead. That great big gruff ballooned wanker. He used to stomp around like a tortoise in a traffic jam, and when seated, his beached whale blubber would often get stuck in the office chair. Flapping, huffing and puffing, the charge nurse had to help him up, so he could devour the morning tea shouts, to none of which he ever contributed.

Everyone was intimidated by him and who on Earth was Fanny to question his malpractice that day?

The old dear lived for three days, and Fanny heard she enjoyed many lovely meals and visitors. She had no family, but it seemed everyone wanted to take a look at the lady who came back from the dead.

If the old dear hadn't cried out to those young recruits, Fanny often wondered if the pathologist would have noticed something from the 'corner of his eye', as he raised the saw to open her chest.

What was Fanny's 'out of the corner of her eye' moment?

You get a choice of three things to consider:

1. She took a shallow breath
2. She passed wind; or
3. She asked for a cup of tea.

The moral of the tale is to make sure you are really dead before you are autopsied, buried or burned alive.

Fanny Fact:
Are They Dead or Not?

Severe hypothermia is where the body drops below twenty-eight degrees celsius and it can give a person the appearance of being dead.

Declaring someone dead can make for a very embarrassing moment if they aren't.

Take the case of the ninety-one-year-old Polish woman called Janina Kolkiewicz, who spent eleven hours in the freezing mortuary chamber.

She too, was found doing the 'get me out of here' jig in her body bag; nothing a cup of hot soup and couple of pancakes couldn't fix though.

Additionally, a doctor by the name of Anna Bangholme fell head first through the ice after losing control of her skis in Norway in 1999.

When she was finally chopped out of the ice, eighty minutes later, she was luckily surrounded by her medical colleagues, who immediately performed CPR. Her core body temperature was measured at thirteen point seven degrees Celsius and she showed no signs of life.

She was transferred to hospital and slowly warmed up until her heart started to beat again.

This was a true miracle, wasn't it?

Today, she is fit and well, and the Fannies think an ice cream should be named after this amazing woman.

Tale 2:
Schlong Wong

There was once a doc, the Fannies nicknamed
'Schlong Wong'
you've guessed it, he emigrated, all the way from
Hong Kong.
As you fall off your chair, reading the tale of his
sociopathic lair,
a predatory monster who thought he could do no wrong.

The vulnerable women all fell at his feet, Schlong's 'love
bombing' ways, so sugary sweet.
Like a basketball player, who shoots for his hoop, Schlong's
women were sadly plugged up with his gloop.

This created a lot of little Wong clones, the outcome of false
promises, during their passionate moans.
Those poor, naive women, all under his spell, none of them
knew, that their life would soon be hell.

Why, this isn't the end of his far-fetching story, it's just the beginning of Wong's sociopathic glory.
The pig, he was bonking all over the land, he hardly felt the need to jerk off with his hand.

He shagged the 'naive' from behind his locked door, on top of his desk, or on his semen-stained floor.
A dangling gold key was a warning, 'don't knock, I'm busy in meetings, and so is my cock!'

Continuing on, with his heart-wrenching crimes, his good looks and charms had them queuing in lines.
He used and abused with his almighty power, and when on his own, he'd wank off in his ivory tower.

One day by surprise, a new nurse applied, unaware she was Schlong Wong's next victim and ride.
She told Fanny of the interview, for her new role, peering from behind her CV, his only query was, "How fresh is your hole?"

An evening meeting, Schlong charmingly arranged, she thought quite naïvely, 'well, he doesn't seem deranged,'
The discussion then left her, in part, quite confused, as she continued her tale, Fanny felt quite bemused.

Before her stunned eyes, as the interview played out, Schlong then gave her his 'look', and then flopped it all out.
He proceeded to lean back, and rock in his chair, adding her to his 'golden key' lair.

He continued to wank off his great big Schlong cock, while
asking her questions, he rhythmically rocked.
When he was finished, he wiped himself off, that fucking
disgusting slippery sloth.

There were many complaints about that health sector, nothing
ever got resolved, why?
He was having his way with the nursing director.

We all know that things have a habit of turning around, as
karma unfolded, he went underground.
He chose the most weakened, leaving the others behind, then
set up a home, the biggest he could find.

Where they shared his big cock, and they did as he told, the
investigative trail was now icy cold.
Fanny isn't a liar, she promises this story is true,
in the town where it happened, perhaps a town near you?

She even went public, by going to the media, when Wong
found out, he quickly went on Expedia.
He moved out of town, as quick as he could, creating a new
and improved persona falsehood.

So Fanny would like to put your minds at some ease, she
asks you to be discerning, as you read her poetic pleas.
Be wary of other Schlong Wong's, and their self-serving
ways, you're better off socialising, with those fabulous gays.

Tale 3:

We Wish You a Merry Christmas and a Happy New Rear

Once upon a Christmas time…

Fanny just loved Christmas. It was her favourite time of the year.

She just couldn't get enough of the tinsel, twinkling fairy lights, cheesy ballads, eggnog and candy canes. She especially loved the snowflakes that began to fall, just in time for the holiday season. Sometimes she would wake up and open her curtains to find the ground covered in snow. It brings a tear to her eye thinking about that happy time.

One particular Christmas, everything changed for our dear Fanny.

She now drowns her holiday spirit in a different type of spirit!

The patients also loved Christmas, and they came in droves, mostly for their Christmas dinner.

The A&E heaved with customers seeking a respite from reality outside the hospital walls. For some, Christmas was the saddest time of the year.

What better place to seek an escape from the poverty of family violence, loneliness and financial burden.

A place where people cared, and if you acted sick enough, you might even get a bed for the night.

One of the doctors would dress up as Santa and give out gifts to the families who returned year after year.

Fanny thought, if they had the courage to come in and admit emotional defeat by feigning their child's or their own illness, then they deserved as much respect as Fanny and the other staff could muster.

It broke Fanny's heart, when a father turned up with his young son. It was clear they were very poor. His love for his son was obvious.

He said they ate dog food to survive, and Fanny believed him, because she thought she could smell the taint of Chum on his breath.

Fanny gave them the best Christmas present for his son's worsening 'asthma.' She got the child admitted, knowing they would have a Christmas dinner, and extra gifts from Santa (maybe even a squeaky toy!).

While Fanny was in the A&E, she worked with a colleague called Dick. They became great friends, and Fanny was thrilled when he got promoted to charge nurse.

With a name like Dick, you wouldn't expect him to have worked several years in a sexual health clinic, but that was exactly where he came from.

One day, Dick decided he had 'Gonorrhoea-d 'off the place, and so 'Chlamydia-ed' the hell out of there.

He said he was tired from the frustration of trying to treat and educate randy teenagers.

"If ye don't take this medication, yer cock (females heard the other C word) will continue to drip like a fucked fridge."

Most would eventually comply.

Dick was a smoking, whisky-drinking Scott, with an accent as thick as his marshmallow bottom.

He was a most exquisitely colourful gay, and his man-scaping sense of style surpassed even her own. The only thing that didn't match was his rotunda shape.

He screamed of hypertension and diabetes, and when Fanny questioned his health, he replied.

"Don't care darling, I'm here for a good time, not a long time."

His broad Scottish accent would sing... and sing he would.

Dick just loved the sound of his own voice and he pranced around the department singing Madonna songs at the top of his voice. There was nothing funnier than seeing him waltz up to an elderly spinster, pointing his finger and singing.

"Like a virgin, touched for the very first time... and how are we today, darling?"

The look on her face was priceless.

He was like a rainbow on steroids, and he shone as brightly at work as he did outside of it. He had an array of lovers, and he always carried a photo of his latest toy boy.

One particular Christmas time, a distinguished patient was bought in because of a very precarious 'Christmas situation.'

Dick described him as a silver fox, because of his 'Christmas situation,' he was immediately put into Dick's capable hands.

Dick's song of the day just happened to be a tune he had uploaded; 'A Chillin in the Brown.'

"Good afternoon dear," said Lord Windy-bottom.

"And a chillin in the brown day to you, my fine sir, now, let's see if we cannae get to the bahoochie of what troubles ye."

Lord Windy-bottom was clearly embarrassed.

He then confessed.

"My dear, I have a very accepting wife, and we are the best of friends, even though I'm a little more the other way inclined. Somewhat like yourself, if you don't mind me saying so, my wife, on occasion, assists me to 'tickle my fancy,' and today that bit of fun got a little out of hand. While we were decorating the Christmas tree, I asked her to be my stallion, and I her mare. After a bit of horsing around, we accidently got the recently-acquired new appendage stuck inside my rectum."

"Oh neigh, neigh," said Dick, laughing, "well, we'd better get in there and get it out, before it rusts your craic darling."

Dick then fetched Fanny to assist him in the upcoming examination.

Fanny and Dick both looked at each other and squirmed.

Dick tried to make light of the situation.

"Hopefully that nozzle stays where it is darling, or Fanny and I may need to put on some protective armour, to protect us from the chocolate snowflakes spraying everywhere."

Dick and Fanny then arranged for his transfer to the operating theatre.

While they were waiting, Lord Windy-bottom showed them photos of his grandchildren. Fanny wondered if they would mention the lack of Christmas snow that year.

"I'm afraid it wasn't possible my dears, because the can is stuck up my arse!"

Fanny shuddered at the thought.

Dick was clearly unfazed. He told Fanny that generally the anaesthetic works a treat.

It relaxes the anal sphincter, allowing the object to slip out.

Lord Windy-bottom eventually became more relaxed in Fanny and Dick's company. He turned and said, "I am well known in social circles and I implore you to respect my confidentiality in this regard."

"Of course," they both replied.

No one would believe them anyway.

"I haven't been completely honest with you both," he went on, "there are some further additions in my back passage."

Before he could go any further, things took a drastic turn for the worse.

"Help me! help me!" he grimaced, "I'm afraid it's gone completely in…"

Fanny rang theatre to inform them of the urgency of the situation. Meanwhile, Dick attempted to reassure him.

"Try not to worry too much darling, I've seen this a hundred times before, some people propel everything bar the kitchen sink up there."

A bowel surgeon who went by the pseudonym 'What Goes Up Must Come Down' soon arrived.

He gently examined the patient and suddenly felt his finger hook onto something hard.

He enquired further, "Sir, before I proceed, I need you to be completely honest with me. What other festive condiments have been placed inside your rectum?"

Fanny and Dick looked intrigued as the Lord proceeded to tell the surgeon what else had been put into his nether regions.

"By hook or by crook, we will do our best to return yer bowel to its former self," reassured Dick.

He looked at the surgeon, who was rolling his eyes at Dick's terrible joke.

Fanny felt flattened by this latest information and her Christmas was beginning to lose its yuletide spark.

The can was successfully removed that day, along with several candy canes, tinsel and two Christmas baubles.

The surgeon informed the Lord that the candy canes had partially melted and prescribed some laxatives to assist the passage of the sticky excrement. He said not to worry if his faecal matter was tinged pink and white for a few days to come.

The Lord went home to his Lady with his dignity, and rectum intact, and Fanny went home to throw out her candy canes. She knew she could never suck on one again without imagining the bitter taste of poop.

Dick turned up the following day, singing a new Christmas song.

"Who can take a snow can, and sprinkle it with poo…
How it even got in there, is a miracle or two.
The candy man can, the candy man did,
And he mixed it with love, to make his world feel good.

Who can take a candy stick, and poke it up his craic,
Lots of little candy canes, some hung on his sack.
The candy man can, the candy man did,
And with a little help from his wife, it made his world feel
good."

Fanny Fact:
The Risks of Inserting Oddities in One's Bum

The Fannies would like you to know that inserting objects into one's back passage is not really a great idea.

If you have to shove something up your chocolate starfish, it should not have jagged edges.

Inserting objects can lead to permanent damage, including rupture of the bowel, bowel prolapse, bleeding, faecal incontinence, infection, and, worst case scenario, you may need a colostomy bag for the rest of your life.

Is it really worth it? The Fannies ask you.

If this object is going to be a schlong, then make sure you give it a good wash with antibacterial soap before sticking it into another orifice, especially into someone's cake hole.

Cross contamination can occur, and your partner will also look like they have been eating chocolate brownies for afternoon tea.

The safest way to use any object for sexual pleasure is to buy from a reputable manufacturer. These are designed to not damage your 'pleasure pipe'. The manufacturers employ people to test these toys before they go on the market, so you can rest assured, they are fully safe to use.

The Fannies have seen many bizarre objects inserted into the 'rusty bullet hole' over their various stints working in A&E departments.

For the readers' entertainment, here are 'butt' a few:

- A pair of salad tongs
- Mobile phones (that rang, but no one answered)
- A live WW2 artillery shell. (The man who inserted the live shell was apparently trying to push his haemorrhoids back up into place, when it suddenly shot up inside him and got stuck in his colon.
- A bomb squad was brought into the hospital to assist with the removal of the said shell).

Tale 4:
Ode to the Spinster Bitches

Once upon a time…

The Fannies had come across many misses, those devoid
of boys' and girls' kisses.
They spat and they cursed, showing little compassion,
they seemed out of place, as they were out of fashion.

A poor choice of vocation for some left unwed, the
reason confusing, and best left unsaid.
Like nuns in the orphanage, brutal and cruel, lacking in
empathy, typical 'old school'.

The spinster did nowt to calm down her fears, "bear
down now young lady and dry those fake tears,
You're just having a baby, for heaven's sake,
and we don't want the wed mothers to wake."

A punishment for being single, in the family way, she
refused her young patient pain relief that day.
She then left the ward with her spinster bitch friend,
leaving Fanny alone with the labour to tend.

The poor junior nurses were treated like slaves, the evil
old spinsters were just so depraved.
Some should have been summoned into the court dock,
while this poem may trigger a memory to shock.

Their cruel, crooked practice went often unquestioned, a
theme at the pub that would always get mentioned.
The cure for those witches, a passionate screw, followed
on by an orgasm or two.

The GPs that lived in that country location, weren't that
much better in their chosen vocation.
'Going into labour' always got in the way, of their plans
to go golfing on that birthing day.

While notorious for his episiotomy ways, this particular
doctor would lengthen their stays.
To ensure extra time at his country club meeting, "I'm
doing this madam, so please stop your bleating."

Then grabbing his gleaming surgical secateurs, he still
went ahead while ignoring her tears.
No permission required, it was his narcissistic way, the
poor pleading woman had no bloody say.

Her legs splayed and helpless, hung up by a belt, he split
her in two as she cried out and yelped.
"Go to hell you old bastard, you arrogant prick, go fuck
those old spinsters, with your shrivelled-up dick."

Many were lovely, not all of them bad, but most were
quite ugly, lonely and sad.
They forgot they deserved a good life for themselves,
instead ending up, on a dusty old shelf.

Tale 5:
Dot's Dilemma

Once upon a winter time…

Fanny was working in a geriatric ward, caring for those who had come in with their winter ailments. Sadly, many of the old dears actually feigned their illnesses, as winter could be a very lonely time.

They were seeking a nurse's tender loving care, and Fanny made sure they got truckloads.

Fanny loved working with the elderly, and although rushed off her feet, she would always try and make time to chat with them.

"How are you feeling this morning Nora? You're looking much perkier, and your cheeks are full of colour," Fanny said.

"Perkier? Are you taking the piss? I feel like shit, and if I had my way I'd be dead, just kill me now," snapped Nora.

"Oh, please don't be like that Nora," Fanny replied, "you still have a lot of life left in your lovely old bones."

"Fuck off!" screeched Nora.

She was so loud that her angry spittle hit Fanny in the face.

"Kill me now, kill me now, kill me now!" Nora continued to scream.

Nora wore a matted, snowy white poodle perm, with a poorly executed fading purple rinse.

No one was allowed near her to give it a gentle brush. It was because she said everything hurt too much, even her hair.

On good days, Nora had a great sense of humour, but clearly today wasn't the time to be 'fannying' around.

"Why don't you throw some of that rinse on your snowy white pubes Nora?" laughed Fanny.

"Fuck off."

Fanny felt bad, as she was only trying to lighten the mood. There was nothing more Fanny could do to comfort her, so she left the bedside, while Nora's "kill me now" screech continued to echo throughout the ward.

The thought of getting to that age and being in Nora's state of mind and body made Fanny panic about what old age might look like for her.

Nora was saggy skin hanging off bone, and clearly hadn't had a decent meal for months. She had two rotting bottom front teeth that stood alone in her gummy sunken mouth. She told Fanny quite blatantly that her husband was also rotting six feet under.

When clear in mind, Nora expressed that she really wanted to die. She said she was done with today's uncaring world and, to be honest, Fanny sympathised and somewhat agreed with her. Nora had bought a burial plot at the local cemetery and couldn't wait to be reunited with her husband.

"I'll get to go on top of him one last time," she joked. Fanny laughed and liked her even more after that.

Later that day, Fanny took a moment's reprieve at the nursing station. It was its usual hectic self; the duty doctor was barking orders while throwing medication charts in her direction.

"Nurse, get this antibiotic for my patient right now, and I mean now, not later!"

"What did your last slave die of?" whispered Fanny, as she sipped her lukewarm tea.

"What did you say, nurse?" he growled.

His stale coffee breath and food-coated teeth made her want to heave.

"Absolutely nothing," she muttered, as he swung around and stormed towards the exit.

As he disappeared from view, Fanny couldn't help but have the last word.

"Another Shlong Prick," she said, while giving the two fingered Fanny salute.

Fanny was grateful for her sense of humour. It had saved her on many occasions, and on that particular day she was going to need it.

Fanny's health care assistant, 'Dot', came pounding towards her to perform the handover of the morning's work.

Dot was a big busted, heavy set woman, who heaved and weaved her large frame about like a Trojan. She was as strong as an ox, but as gentle as a new born lamb with the patients.

Fanny always knew where to find her; her bellowing laugh could be heard from one end of the ward to the other.

Dot pulled her crumpled nursing notes out of her uniform

pocket and began to read in typical Dot fashion.

"Bed 6, Freda shit-for-Sundays, seventy-five years old, admitted last night with impacted constipation, she's since been evacuated, and at the last count has had her seventh shit of the day, it was absolutely fucking massive Fanny, looked like it had come from a rhino.

Bed 7, Mrs Morbidly Obese with abdominal distention, I swear there must be a full-term baby in there, and she's about to pop. I think it's just wind, because she's just had a fart so explosive, the windows nearly bloody shattered. Perhaps she shot that baby out at the same time too, but there is no sign of it anywhere," she laughed.

"Oh, and last but not least is bed 8, kill me now Nora, an eighty-year-old widow, with depression and loss of appetite."

Dot then went on.

"I'm really worried about her, Fanny. She looks pale and just doesn't want to eat. She feels quite cold, so I've put a couple of extra blankets on her. I've tried her with a cup of tea, and that sieved cat sick they send us from the kitchen, but she just keeps spitting it out onto her nightgown."

"I'd probably spit it out too, it looks absolutely foul," replied Fanny, "she still has some life in her yet Dot, so just keep trying to tempt her. Maybe a bit of yogurt would go down better?"

Dot agreed and waltzed off to the kitchen to fetch the yogurt. Another couple of hours flew by and Fanny rushed to put pen to paper while Dot got on with the ward's demands.

Dot was an amazing 'head down, bum up' woman and as Fanny hadn't found the time to get back to her patients, she banked on Dot to holler in case of emergency.

Dot was minutes from finishing her shift when she arrived with a final patient handover.

"Freda shit for Sundays is now two stone lighter, Mrs

Morbidly Obese has been given the all clear to go home tomorrow, before she shatters any more windows... I tried Nora with some yogurt, but the same thing happened, she kept spitting it out, I've left the spoon in her hand, hoping she will eat some, maybe you could pop down to see her before we finish?"

"Let's go now," answered Fanny.

The ward was called a Nightingale Ward, a huge, sterile room, with beds on either side, all lined up in uniform precision. Patients sat compliantly for the doctors' visits, and it was a mad rush to have them in pristine condition before they arrived.

Nora's floral curtains were still pulled around her, because she was such a disruption to the other patients.

Together they hauled them back.

"See Fanny? It's all over her nightgown again," said Dot. She moved in to wipe the caked food that was dribbling and drying at the corners of Nora's mouth.

Fanny leaned in to take a closer look at Nora... then she turned to Dot.

"Dot," she whispered, "come with me, around the curtain."

"Wait a minute," replied Dot, "I want to make her more

comfortable first. God, she's stiff," Dot sighed, as she struggled to settle her.

"Nora, bend a bit love. You're not making it very easy for me."

Nora remained quietly compliant for a change.

"Dot, can you please come outside the curtain!" Fanny said more insistently.

Fanny then dragged Dot back to the nurse's station.

"Dot, I hate to be the bearer of bad news, but Nora is dead, as dead as a door knob, and by the looks of her, I would say she has been dead for some time."

Fanny then started laughing so hard she snorted like a ravenous pig.

"Dead? She can't be! I've been trying to feed her all morning, and I've only just sat her up for some yogurt!" stammered Dot.

Dot's face then whitened, her body stiffening into a rigor mortis stance somewhat similar to that of kill me now Nora.

Fanny sat Dot down and coaxed her to eventually see the funny side of the situation, but it took a few weeks before Dot was able to crack a joke about that day.

"Anyone fancy a 'stiff' drink after work"?

Nora got her final wish and was laid to rest on top of 'Mr kill me now' one last time.

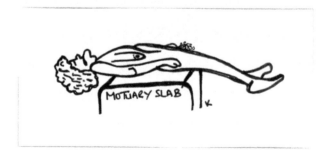

Fanny Fact:
Rigor Mortis Explained

Did you know that after you pop your clogs, rigor mortis affects the facial muscles first (similar to ageing movie stars who have been 'botoxed').

The rigor mortis effect then spreads to other parts of the body, making you as stiff as a board, until the decomposition starts. This takes up to forty-eight hours and occurs because your metabolism is still working.

Poor old Nora's cake hole was clearly in the state of rigor mortis at the time Dot was trying to feed her, her mouth as agape as the English Channel tunnel. She was clearly no longer hungry, and in no state to swallow anything.

Men reading this Fanny fact may be wondering, does rigor mortis affects one's shlong?

Why, yes, it does, say the Fannies.

When you drop off the twig, you may experience an unusable stiffy.

"What a waste," say the Fannies.

However, it's got to be good news for anyone into necrophilia. They would be in for the ride of their life, now, wouldn't they!

N.B. The Fannies do not defend necrophilia, as it is highly illegal and somewhat disrespectful, don't you think?

Tale 6:
Anu's Palace

Once upon a time…

The two Fannies decided to gift the reader a little 'Bo Peep', into their private world.

As you read on, you will visualise and decide which one of the Fannies you resonate with the most. We think you will resonate with both of them, as they are both fabulous in their own unique ways.

Meet 'Fanny One'.

She is all the colours of the rainbow, and she knows that she sticks out like an ingrown toenail in the corporate world.

Her rainbow streaked hair flows as freely as her vibrant personality.

Her tree of life tattoo has bulged proudly with each child she has carried.

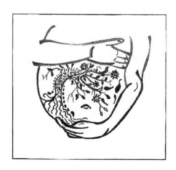

Sadly for Fanny, that tattoo now resembles a fallen tree stump, and she is hoping the money from this book can re-plant the tree back in its rightful place.

She has driven the same old Ford Cortina for as long as she can remember.

Her brood surprised her one day by painting it the same colour as her hair.

Her life's mission is to heal the broken, one heartbeat at a time. Sometimes she forgets it is her own heart that needs healing the most.

As she sprinkles her fairy godmother dust over everyone and everything, her friend Fanny gently reminds her.

"Remember to save some of that fairy dust for yourself, hon."

Fanny Two...

She stands out in a crowd, and that is exactly how she likes it. She is her own theatre production and she acts in every scene.

She has been turning heads her entire life, and her catlike hazel eyes have made many a grown man cry.

When Fanny Two cries, it is elegance personified.

While her friend, Fanny One, snots and wails like a hyena

on heat, this Fanny sheds silent tears, catching them quickly before they mess with her plum-blushed cheeks.

Her black modette bob has been her signature look forever. Thirty years later, it is still preened to perfection, as is her other bob!

Her money is spent on the best that money can buy.

Clothes, shoes, handbags, sunglasses, make-up, and men. Sometimes, her sunglasses are a little fogged up when it comes to choosing men.

She rises early, making herself a pot of tea, and refilling her cup several times over, she prepares for the day ahead.

She briefly scowls at the loss of her youth in the mirror. What she doesn't realise is this; the lines of her face reflect back something far more beautiful; the wisdom of her life experiences.

With the skill of a painter, she creates her face, the same way an artist paints a scene. She is so skilled at her craft that when she leaves the house, the whole world breaks out into applause. Fanny is proudly poised in a sassy, stylish sort of way and when together, the Fannies tenderly nurture the other's nature. In the parallel experiences of their lives, they were destined to be the best of friends.

The two Fannies' corporate lives took them from one end

of the country to the other. On their long-haul trips, they loved the opportunity to chat about the uncanny similarities in both their professional and personal lives.

What you need to know about the two Fannies, is that they have a penchant for making more fun of themselves than they ever would of others.

They have found the 'Fanny funny side' of their ageing bodies, in particular, the spaniel ears that now hang against their chests.

'Fanny One' said her nipples could stretch to the end of her garden path, probably caused by one of her children's last suckles as they rushed to catch the school bus.

They once got clothes pegs and grabbed their fish fillets of facial skin. When finished, they resembled a clothing line of saggy wet washing, but, by God, it took twenty years off them.

The Fannies are accepting of the good, the bad, and the ugly in life. However, their biggest burden is the shipwreck that lies at the bottom of their sea.

That part of their bodies has taken a bashing, pounding, stretching, pulling and pushing.

We all know what happens with shipwrecks, don't we? They end up with a leaky hull!

When inebriated, they describe their 'leaking hull' as being of Niagara proportions.

At other times, after a cough or giggle, it is no more uncomfortable than lying in the post-coital wet spot.

You're not going to believe this, dear reader, but after writing this book, the Fannies researched for plagiarism to ensure their names were completely unique. Lo and behold, they found out that there is an actual shipwreck that lies at the bottom of the ocean, off the west coast of Ohio and it is called the 'Two Fannies!' If that isn't a sign for them to put this book out into the world, they don't know what is!

For entertainment value, they wish to tell you that their 'pissed piss,' could fill an entire swimming pool.

If you ever get to meet the two Fannies while out on the town, they are known as the 'Two Tenors,' and this has nothing to do with their karaoke voices.

On one of those odd occasions, where they have forgotten to 'tenor pad up,' you might want to put on a life jacket and step out of the way before you find yourself drowning in the 'Fanny shipwreck'.

It could be worse; they could be middle-aged men with prostates the size of lemons, and not be able to piss a single drop.

On one particular day, they decided to check out of the office early, as they had had enough of the humourless robots.

"Kill me now," Fanny emailed her friend.

"I concur," Fanny answered, which was the code to pack up and to go to one of their made- up meetings.

There were only two things on the meeting agenda; Prosecco followed by a decent curry.

I am sure by now you have figured out which one of them is vegan.

The only meat that ever entered her mouth was the throbbing kind, and even that made her gag. She is still applying her homemade herbal balm to both sets of split lips, resulting from the escapades with her last lover.

Fanny two gave Fanny one the following advice.

"Remember Fanny, little man all dick, big man no dick."

Both Fannies had fallen hard for a pretender or two, those who pretended at everything they said, and everything they did. They still nurture the scars, as they know you do your own.

After a few too many Proseccos at the local bar, they inevitably got hungry.

"Fancy an Indian, hon?" slurred Fanny.

"I'd much rather shag an Englishman, Fanny. I prefer a banger in my mash to a chicken in my korma," she laughed, cheekily.

Tears of snotty laughter ran down both their faces, until they realised somewhat urgently, that it was 'Niagara' time. Linking arms and crossing their legs, they staggered towards the rest room.

Following the waterfall moment, they made their way to the recently-opened Indian restaurant. As they walked through the glimmering gold doors, a godlike creature called Anu greeted them.

Atop his head was a beautiful coiffured golden turban. Beneath this was an exquisitely manicured moustache above a flowing beard. His white robe covered the baggy harem trousers that rested atop his intricately-embroidered slippers. His perfectly proportioned porcelain teeth blinded them with his happiness.

"Hello, young ladies. Table for two?" he greeted with his wobbly head.

Once upon a time, an inebriated Fanny tried to assist another waiter with his wobbly head.

She told him it gave her motion sickness, so she grabbed it and held it still. She had to be reminded later that the gesture was more of a custom than a nervous tic.

"Anu, we are so hungry we could eat a scabby cow," said Fanny.

"No scabby cows here, ladies" he replied.

He then handed them the menus.

The Fannies laughed, and their curries soon arrived.

Using their naan like a soup spoon, they ravenously tucked in. One of the Fannies suddenly looked up, a small frown appearing as she began to recall a memory, a 'Fanny tale' from another Indian restaurant.

She screamed at her friend to listen, as she took a swig of Prosecco, and proceeded to tell her tale.

This Fanny was known for her creative expression and it came as no surprise when she looked at her friend and broke into a limerick:

There once was a lady I have called Mrs Crème,
her clothes were nosh posh, and her teeth white-pristine,
The day after ingesting, most of her curry,
to her husband she screamed; "get me to the doctor, quick hurry."

Her private physician met her at his clinic door,
she presented the leftover slop she had eaten the night before.
"Oh, God, my dear woman," he ushered her in quick,
with a voice that spoke of arrogance, "I get rich off my
patients" prick.

She projectiled herself all over his clinic,
both ends of her pipes spurting out by the minute.
"I diagnose food poisoning, we will get an investigation."
The doc couriered the evidence, to the nearest police station.

A few days later, he telephoned her estate,
politely apologising for the test being so late.
He went onto explain the reason for its delay,
the testing had confused them, in a scientific sort of way.

"Tell me the bad news, as I trust you with my life,"
Mr Crème also sat there, to support his ailing wife.
"Listen intently, my dear, what I have to tell is shocking."
Mrs Crème was so fearful, she began rocking.

"What on Earth do you mean? Am I dying, dear doc?"
"No, my dear woman, what you've eaten, has come out of a
cock!
The protein ingested, hasn't come from animal meat,"
Mrs Crème then screamed and fell right off her seat.

Fanny continued the tale that chills,
how the Dr treated Mrs Crème, with lots of antibiotic pills.
And as for the restaurant, it is no longer there,
The owner's in jail, and the restaurant's now bare.

There are penises graffitied all over its walls,
the Crème's compensated, by the court halls.
Fanny then looked at her friend, her face in dismay,
as she continued to tell, of what happened that day.

"Oh my god Fanny, is this tale really true?"
"It is the truth, the whole truth, and nothing but the truth,"
laughed Fanny.

The lovely Anu then returned to their table.

"Ladies!" he exclaimed, "what is wrong with your curry?
Why do you not swallow?"

"We've swallowed enough, Anu" they laughed
hysterically.

"So has Mrs Crème!" Fanny whispered to her friend.

Apparently, seven employees' DNA was retrieved from
the said curry, and poor Mrs Crème required psychological
intervention for years to 'cum'.

All because she believed it was too un-ladylike to
swallow.

The moral of this tale is this; while you may make a
promise to yourself that you will never swallow, you may have
un-semeningly already had your protein shot!

Fanny Fact:
Getting to Know One's Cum!

The Fannies wish you to know, that the smell of a man's spoof cannot be changed. It will never taste like a cream donut, or if you are indigenous, a chocolate brownie.

Apparently, if you are a smoker, the taste can be a little off. The Fannies imagine it's a bit like kissing an ashtray at both ends.

There are two trillion of those tadpole swimmers, and seven point five litres of the muff-filling stuff. The calorific value isn't actually that bad – five to ten calories – so there is no excuse not to swallow! But the choice is yours.

What makes the sperm thin and slippery, or thick and gloopy? It comes down to hydration, or a mechanism where prostate enzymes meet sperm and mix it up to change the consistency. A bit like making yourself a milkshake. If they hang out in the depository bank of a 'Fanny', it liquefies further, and becomes more mobile.

Want to make a baby? Put a plug in that bathtub!

The Fannies would like you gentlemen to know that no harm has 'cum' to any men during the retrieval of these Fanny facts.

Tale 7:
Ode to the Orderlies

Once upon a time, the Fannies met a humble man called
Mohamad…

Mohamad was now living in a country
He had for so long waited,
While he prayed for peace for the many,
Who his faith they judged and hated.

Mohamad, his children, and his wife,
All escaped years of war-torn strife.
He was polite as he was kind and giving,
Becoming an orderly was his chosen living.

He got to trust the Fannies well,
And would sometimes share his past torment and hell.
He told them tales of his birthplace,
And as he reminisced, sadness appeared on his face.

One day the Fannies were invited to his dwelling,
In a suburb, rich with buying and selling.
The pair both excited, as they knocked on his door,
And what happened next, left the Fannies in awe.

The extended family welcomed them inside,
While Mohamad introduced them, with all of his pride.
They then sat down, on his rug laden floor,
As the Fannies took their seats, he closed the lounge door.

Dozens of eyes now proceeded to stare,
Their visit was considered an honourable affair.
They wanted to leave, as they felt overcome,
But food was delivered, and they had to eat some.

They gratefully accepted their plates and their spoon,
While soon realising; their bellies had no room!
They had earlier stopped at a local café,
And consumed a 'full English' along the way.

Their plates were layered up with sweet and spicy,
Naan, fruit and dates, with chicken ricey.
After they left , they soon had to stop,
To splutter up, their undigested plop.

Later at work, Fanny all of a rush,
She called to Mohamed to help with a push,
The patient to move was particularly obese,
A lady who wished her sad life would decease.

Fanny and Mohamad, took her on the journey,
Pushing with might, her big frame on the gurney.
While Fanny walked beside, observing her condition,
Something slapped against her thigh, without any permission.

A large elephant's ear, a- swinging in the breeze,
'Was the circus in town?' Fanny thought with unease.
She then asked Mohamad to stop for a rest,
So she could take discreet measures, to retrieve the huge
breast.

Fanny asked Mohamad, to please turn his back,
As she used all her 'oomph' to lift up the skinned sack.
Obediently Mohamad, looked down to his feet,
As Fanny prepared to pull back the bed sheet.

She stuffed back the tit, as you would stuff a chicken,
And for weeks after, it put Fanny off the Colonel's finger
lickin.
The patient never noticed, her missing body part,
Her huge swinging tit was nothing compared to her ailing
heart.

So Fanny's only mission,
Was to keep Mohamad and the patient's dignity intact.
Look inside the middle of the book,
For your Fanny 'tit' Fanny fact.

Tale 8:
The Banana Split Slit

Once upon a time…

In another land very far away, Fanny had not long since graduated. She was living her dream of being an idealistic eager beaver.

She was up for any and all challenges in her new found career, and ready to get stuck into everything that came her way. The above word 'stuck' is fitting, given the tale you are about to read. Nothing could shock this girl, or so she thought!

Like a song that you just can't get out of your head, the term 'There ain't nowt so strange as folk' may also get 'stuck' inside yours.

The Fannies wonder why people appear to have nothing better to do than to inflict such harm upon their bodies… and in the strangest of ways. It was a human phenomenon they happened to witness regularly throughout their nursing careers.

On one particular 'eager beaver' day, a man was brought in by ambulance with a kitchen footstool attached to him. It was a sight to see it lying in bed with him. He just couldn't part himself from it. Apparently he had slipped on a wet floor and one of the stool legs had tragically lodged within.

That chair leg apparently cleverly targeted his bum hole because, as he slipped, his cheeks parted company, and the leg found its way right on in there. That poor, accident prone bugger had got himself *well and truly* buggered.

Fanny felt so sorry for him, and all the other patients that objects had a habit of just finding their way inside. She became very mindful of where she began to sit, just in case something might find its way into her.

Oh, my God, she thought. *I'm at double the risk of mishap.*

Every shift was unique, and this particular one didn't fail to disappoint.

"Fanny, can you please assist me?" asked the doctor.

"I've got something to show you, and you can rest assured you will never see anything like this again," he smirked.

Fanny was intrigued, because she thought she had seen it all, but by God, this was the icing on the cake.

The doctor was incredibly hot to trot, and made the nurses' fannies tingle like 'Pop Rocks' as they begin to melt on your tongue. They all drooled over him, and he made Fanny weak at the knees.

He had shoulder-length sweeping, golden locks and he did the right thing by the nurses: instead of tying them back into a ponytail (look out for the pony in a later tale), he constantly ran his fingers through those golden tresses, sweeping them off his shoulders like a Hollywood superstar. This exposed the perfection of his tanned, chiselled face. Fanny wished he would run his fingers through her 'tingle.'

He was stomach crunching six-pack athletic, and the nurses dreamed about what secrets and treasures hid beneath his crisp white doctor's coat.

Fanny imagined her tongue sliding up and down his chiselled peaks and valleys, while her 'Pop Rocks' exploded over and over like a display of fireworks.

One of her colleagues waltzed up to Fanny and whispered her own admiration of him as they both watched him 'cat walk' down the corridor to the patient's room.

"I would love to thank Michelangelo for sculpturing him. I bet that 'David' is better in bed than the sack of shit waiting for me at home."

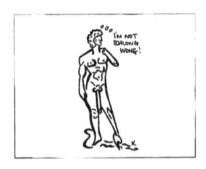

"Me too," Fanny answered.

And now she had been invited into an examination room with him.

What more could she wish for? Fanny's mind boggled and her body 'Pop Rocked', as she went to join him.

"You will need a full-length apron Fanny, a pair of gloves, and don't forget your full-face visor," he instructed.

"Your wish is my command" said Fanny, fluttering her eyelashes.

But David didn't notice.

"Should I keep my knickers on?" she whispered under her heaving breath.

"Excuse me Fanny?" David replied.

It was then she realised that her comment hadn't quite been a whisper at all.

"Should I put an admission sticker on?" she

corrected…Whew!

That was a good save. Fanny gulped.

Fully protected, Fanny now found herself looking far removed from the sexy, knicker less nurse she wanted him to visualise.

The patient was lying with her legs placed into a well-worn pair of metal stirrups, with a sheet modestly covering her.

She was an attractive woman in her twenties, and Fanny imagined she would be beautiful without all that makeup caked on her face.

What was she hiding? Pondered Fanny.

As Fanny introduced herself, she noticed her patient's nicotine stained fingers and chipped red polish on her fingernails. It was also then she noticed something else, a pungent odour coming from beneath the sheet.

As hard as she tried, she could not pinpoint exactly what the smell reminded her of.

She had eaten fish and chips at the café for lunch, so perhaps it was the remnants of that?

She put her hand briefly inside her mask, cupping her hand, to smell her breath, *nope, that's not it,* she thought intrigued.

Her patient was quiet and extremely apprehensive, so Fanny did her best to reassure her and calm her nerves.

The patient continued to barely acknowledge them, preferring instead to stare blankly at the ceiling.

Fanny took her mind off the smell by imagining David bulging beneath his zipper. It was an easy visualisation as David stood next to her, explaining the pending examination to his patient. Fanny tingled with delight and could barely breathe; it was here that her imagination went wild.

Put me up in those stirrups and I will show you my Fanny curtains, then we can go to town together because there is a sale on, and I come real cheap..

The doctor's conversation quickly brought Fanny back down to Earth, and she pulled herself together.

"Fanny is a new nurse and she has come to support you."

The patient nodded, the blush on her cheeks turning crimson. Fanny felt sorry for her; she looked so powerless lying there. Taking her hand, Fanny whispered.

"It's alright, hon, everything is going to be okay."

David then lifted back the sheet, exposing her 'fanny curtains.'

Fanny looked between her patient's legs and became quite puzzled… she couldn't figure out what she was witnessing.

"What on Earth is going on down there? Is it animal, mineral, or vegetable?"

Completely mesmerised, she watched as, one by one, out slipped small, white, curly worms.

Fascinated… Fanny noticed they were all moving! She silently screamed behind her surgical mask.

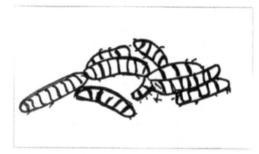

After calming down, Fanny started to strategise.

"Earthworms live in the earth, and thread worms live in the bowel of snotty little kids, so what on Earth could these worms be?" Fanny looked up at David, bewildered.

It was then she noticed David was quietly laughing away to himself, he could see her confusion and was enjoying every single minute of it.

"Let me explain… this unfortunate young lady was having sexual relations and her partner decided to insert a banana 'deep' into her vagina."

Fanny thought he emphasised the word 'deep' for her benefit.

Fanny answered him with the only words she could summon.

"Oh, that's nice."

David then went on.

"She thought it would work its way out naturally, but unfortunately, it has become stuck."

It was then Fanny noticed the flies. They appeared to come from nowhere, and had started to gather and swirl around the edge of her patient's fanny curtains, and on closer observation, she realised that the maggots dropping out of her patient were hatching.

Fanny felt her stomach flip and she quickly turned away, discreetly throwing up within her face mask, which wasn't very discreet at all.

"Unfortunately the banana has caused a maggot infestation, and she will need to go to theatre as soon as possible, Fanny. The object will then be removed, and her vagina washed out."

"Oh, I see." Fanny spluttered.

Her fish and chip lunch now pooling under her chin.

By this stage Fanny wasn't listening. She was busy scanning the room for fly spray.

Beneath the doctor's mask, Fanny could see tears of silent laughter streaming down his cheeks, as they both attempted to retain a sense of professional composure, for the sake of their patient.

"That hot wanker set me up," fumed Fanny.

He continued to 'Fanny finger' the patient's 'banana cream pie,' gently scooping out the maggoty mess, the poor patient stared at the ceiling in an attempt to detach herself from the whole humiliating experience.

All the while, the maggots continued to hatch and buzz.

Fanny thought about the patient's fruit bat partner, wondering where he was in supporting his poor girlfriend. She wanted to tell her patient to give him a taste of his own medicine – an unripe plantain banana experience of his own, so far up his own arse, it comes out of his mouth.

Fanny wanted to grab him by the scruff of his neck, and yell,

"Were you just hungry for a banana split, with the added sprinkle of your nuts on top?"

The moral of this story: don't ever insert a banana, or any

food for that matter, into any orifice, other than your mouth.

It has no nutritional value whatsoever at the other end.

Please also remember that what goes up might not actually come down, and then you become nothing but a fucked-up maggoty mess.

Fanny Fact:
The World's Biggest Banana

The Rhino Horn Plantain from Africa bears a fruit of ginormous proportions.

That banana is up to two feet long (sixty cm), twelve to fourteen inches in diameter (thirty-two cm).

Imagine the flies that could buzz around one of those!

If those bananas are anything like a 'black man's shlong', then it goes without saying, 'once you go black, you never go back!'

This is not racist.

The Fannies did warn you.

Why, Fanny has even checked with her partner Cocoa, who is very proud of his own spectacular bulge.

The Good, The Bad and The Ugly of The Doctor's Tales

Tale 9
The Doctor's Lasting Legacy

This tale actually makes the 'Two Fannies' very uncomfortable, but you have paid for the truth, so here goes another, 'once upon a time'…

Doctor Major has left a profound taste in Fanny's mouth, a very sour one. He had a self-entitled charm with the nurses, but surprisingly, he was professional enough to keep it in his pants. In other ways, he was completely unprofessional, and he could be brutal, particularly to those he labelled 'the attention seekers.'

The so-called attention seekers were those who were frequent flyers to A&E.

One young woman, who came in regularly, was demanding and, at times, very difficult to manage.

Even the ambulance staff would voice that she was a waste of time and resources.

Fanny felt that she was no less deserving than any other patient who wanted to be heard and, more importantly, cared about in their moment of distress.

The young woman was heavily scarred on both wrists and had used a razor blade, yet again, as a cry for help.

Fanny felt that the angst that drove someone to do such a thing must be so distressing.

It was an incredibly busy evening, and Dr Major was working the same shift as Fanny.

Fanny went to tell him that his next patient was waiting, and she found him in the office pouring a cup of coffee. When she told him who was next on the list, he angrily slammed the kettle down.

"I've bloody had enough of this!" he scowled.

Dr Major jumped up and stormed towards the patient's room. He burst in and walked straight up to her.

"Here, watch me!" he said, as he pulled his pen out of his shirt pocket.

Using the pen as if it were a cutting instrument he then demonstrated how to cut her wrists in a way that death would not be painful or prolonged, he then left to return to his coffee, leaving Fanny and the other staff with their mouths agape. Some staff in their unease, suggested he was just joking, and considered it funny. Fanny didn't.

She rode her bike home crying that night.

The most horrible aspect of this tale, is this; Fanny never saw her patient again…

She heard through the police, a couple of years later, that her patient had drowned in an accident. Well, that's what they called it at the time!

Fanny is ashamed for not sticking up for her patient's rights that day.

This was a time in her life when no one questioned those in the white doctor's coat.

Perhaps not even you.

Thankfully times have changed.

Tale 10
"Turn the Boat Back, Captain!"

Once Upon a time…

Not all the doctors were bad. Dr Mike was one of the good ones.

He was exemplary in his kindness, and cared for everyone, and everything, he also loved a social occasion and would turn up to the opening of an envelope, as long as there was a bar and a good story to be told.

Dinner was served a bit too late for Mike at one of those social occasions, he'd had a few too many, on an empty stomach. When his fettucine arrived, he tucked into it with gluttonous ferocity.

Fanny called out to him from the other side of the table, asking if it tasted good. He looked up at her, and what a sight to behold. With glazed eyes he slurred,

"It's dericious, Fanny!"

Fanny and the other guests cried with their very own 'dericiousness,' when they saw his face dripping in creamy sauce.

All of a sudden, the band started playing, and Mike looked up excitedly. He jumped up from his seat and staggered straight onto the dance floor.

He became the venue's entertainment that night as he danced and jived to the music, he had the whole dance floor to himself, because no one else was game enough to join him.

Why? you ask.

With every flick of his head, the creamy gunk flew in different directions. It was strewn all over the dance floor.

Dr Mike was also a magician. He had a habit of calling it a night by disappearing into thin air.

His own "beam me up, Scotty" moment.

"Where did Mike go?"

No one ever saw him leave, ever!

Fanny once asked him why he pulled the disappearing act.

She said it reminded her of a time when someone she loved asked her to marry him, and then in the next breath, 'poofed' himself out of her life.

Mike said his dancing feet knew when to call it a night, and he would discreetly dance his way out of the door, dancing all the way home.

So, if you ever see a man jiving down the road with food caked all over his face, give him a friendly shout.

"Hey, Mike, how was that fettucine?" ... "Dericious!"

Mike had many sad tales of his own, but he paid them no mind; he had made the decision to be happy, no matter what.

"There is always someone worse off than me, Fanny," he would say.

One day, Mike was on a boat trip with a group of old school friends. He'd had a big night at the Port Hotel and the next morning, they were running late to board the boat.

They decided to go straight to the bar for a hair of the dog cure, and it wasn't long before the captain made an urgent announcement.

"If there is a doctor on board, can you please make yourself known."

One of Mike's friends turned and pointed, shaping his hand into a microphone.

He then said in a deep correspondent voice.

"And it's over to you, Mike…"

A little slower than he usually would, Mike sprang into action and made his way to a uniformed member of staff.

"I'm a doctor," he said proudly.

The ship's crew member looked at the unshaven, dishevelled man with some scepticism.

Mike had to reassure him that he was, in fact, the full quid, a real doctor.

He was led to another part of the ship and soon found himself in the middle of a commotion. A tourist had been attacked by a big, nasty, buzzing bee and the recipient of the sting was allergic. Rigor mortis allergic!

Mike told the Fannies he then experienced his own 'out of the corner of his eye' moment. A nurse had also made herself known to the crew and he said she was rather gorgeous.

"Back before I was married, girls, I might have given it a second thought."

Mike and the nurse then went to work as the tourist was in full anaphylactic shock and the outcome looked rather grim.

The captain rushed up to them.

"Excuse me, doctor, do you think I should turn around?"

Without raising his head, Mike lifted his arm and pointed towards the land they had left twenty minutes before.

He then instructed, "Turn the boat back Captain!"

He told the Fannies the patient survived, and when the boat was turned around again, he and the nurse were invited up to the captain's deck. An announcement was made across the entire ship about how they had saved the passenger's life.

His friends never once left the bar and they were grateful for that extra time.

On Mike's return, they cheered at his newfound celebratory status, and Mike joined them as they all sang.

"Yo ho ho and a bottle of rum" (or two) as they travelled back across the water.

Mike told the Fannies,

"Why, I even made the news that night, girls."

One of the Fannies didn't want to dull his moment by telling him that she had also once made the news.

This is the end of the Doctors tales… Naughty buggers weren't they!

Tale 11
Catch Me If You Can

Once upon a time…

In the middle of the night, Fanny woke to her phone ringing. The voice on the other end asked for her immediate presence in the operating theatre. An emergency caesarean section was on the way.

This created a lot of stress for our dear Fanny, as the rule was that you had to be at work within twenty minutes of the call. Fanny would count down the time, and given she had a ten-minute drive, it was always a mad dash to get there.

Her mad dash went something like this: jump up, get dressed, boil kettle, brush teeth, make coffee, grab car keys, rush out of the door forgetting to pee.

Rush back in to pee, rush back out, lock door, run to car, forget work bag, rush back inside to get bag, and so on.

After all that, she forgot to make herself a cup of coffee!

Fanny's driving usually involved lots of cutting corners, running stop signs, screaming through orange lights, and finding a car park close to the hospital entrance.

It also involved the occasional police siren.

Fanny once got a ticket after forgetting to put on her seat belt. She tried to get away with this by saying it restricted her breathing, because of her asthma.

She even once tried showing a bit of her 'spaniel ear' cleavage to get out of paying, but that didn't work either.

Fanny eventually conceded defeat and paid for each and every ticket.

Have you noticed when you are in a rush to get somewhere, everything gets in your way? Trucks, buses, red lights and old people on crossings.

The final straw for Fanny was always the hospital lift. Every single time, it was sitting on the top floor, while she stood on the ground floor, slamming the button. She hoped it might get to her fast, but it never did, it just made her later every time.

Fanny would arrive in theatre, gowned up, with sweat dripping down her face, looking as if she had run through a rainstorm.

"I'm here everybody," she screeched, which was her friendly way of pleading for no one to fire back at her, but someone always did.

"About bloody time," shouted the charge nurse. "You're nothing but a fucking hindrance Fanny."

The obstetrician barely looked up at her, he had clearly been up all night.

His unshaven face had the look of a pit bull; his American snarl could often be heard from one end of the theatre to the other, as he drooled and slavered from behind his mask.

He hated living where he did, and he was always complaining about living in a country with people as dull as the weather. However, 'Pitbull' had signed up for his stint, so was legally bound to the dullness of his current location, but what he didn't realise was that his abhorrent behaviour made the staff feel dull, they hated being in his company, he was rude, aggressive and a complete wanker.

He thought he was untouchable!

Rumour has it, he caught the train into the city on his days off. He was a regular at a popular strip joint, where 'Mr Untouchable' paid to be touched.

It gave the staff some satisfaction that he couldn't find anyone willing to do it for free.

Back in the day, fake tan products left one with a Californian orange appeal, and that is exactly what he looked like, except without the goodness of a real orange.

By this time, Fanny had developed her 'Fanny fingered resilience.'

She wasn't bothered by him at all. His pit bull style was mostly aimed at the junior doctors, whom he left crumbling around him, so much so, Fanny knew of one, that ended up on sick leave. This Doctor eventually came back, medicated, and with a stress-induced nervous tremor.

Any complaints went into the overflowing complaint drawer in the sky. Thrown out and burned with the hospital rubbish.

The Pit Bull was as unprofessional as he was a bully and, even worse than that, he thought he was funny, to boot.

That night, he would 'trump' his so-called funny side in a way that would never be forgotten.

"Move," he barked as he fired his orders in every direction.

"Move it," he scowled.

But no one ever moved fast enough for him. His voice grated on the entire room, like a fingernail scratching down a chalkboard.

Being an obstetrician was an odd choice of specialisation, given his attitude.

The Fannies feel that the self-entitled just love to feed on the vulnerable.

It makes them feel powerful to have control.

(At this point, you might like to go to the Fanny fact on 'Narcissism' for further enlightenment).

The expectant parents were also powerless, and Pit Bull was oblivious to their presence in the room.

He continued his demeaning comments to the staff regardless.

He also had massive paws and it worried Fanny his incision might not be big enough. He dug his way in like he was searching through a sack of spuds, trying to find the right one for his dinner.

"Move out of the way, you stupid nurse," he barked. Fanny was only trying to do her job in assisting him.

He started pulling the baby out of its cocoon, and it was clearly a whopper. He struggled to extract it while Fanny said to herself, be gentle, you orange-tinged twat.

Luckily, the parents-to-be were protected by the shield of the sheet, so were oblivious as to what was going on around them. Fanny got a quick glimpse of the father kissing the mother-to-be gently on the forehead. He was whispering reassuringly into her ear.

Fanny was grateful the sheet was there, because what happened next gave her nightmares for months.

As he pulled the baby out, a sick, twisted expression appeared on his face.

He looked like he was drooling around his mask, she noticed bits of rabid spittle frothing from the corners.

Fanny had turned her back briefly, when she heard him shout,

"Here, catch this if you can!"

Pit Bull hurled the baby towards Fanny, throwing it in the air like a football.

Fanny quickly turned and lunged to catch it. Realising that she still might still drop the slippery new born, she threw her whole-body weight towards the wee tot, ensuring he would land as close to her body as possible.

She had to realign her hands and arms several times to ensure the baby was safely caught.

It was a heart-stopping, breath-holding moment for all those witnessing the horrific ordeal.

"Great catch nurse," laughed Pit Bull.

He then turned away, peeling off his bloodstained gloves.

"Congratulations, you have a bouncing baby boy," he laughed at the parents.

He then threw his gloves on the ground and walked out of the theatre, leaving his tremoring assistant to sew her up.

You could hear a pin drop, as the baby was quickly wrapped and presented to the new parents. (Thankfully, they were none the wiser!)

This incident was the final straw for the entire staff. While he thought himself untouchable, other than the strippers he paid, this time he wasn't so lucky.

The orange faced Oompa-Loompa wanker was finally relieved of all his duties.

Rumour has it, he disappeared somewhere down Sunset Boulevard to mix with those who weren't as dull as those he had left behind.

Fanny wonders if he is still throwing babies from one end of the theatre to the other.

She also wonders if any of them ended up growing up with brain damage, and perhaps even ended up in politics?

More Fabulous Fanny Facts!
You Have Rights

The Fannies would like you to know that times are changing for the better.

Today, you have the right to be heard, and to be treated with dignity. This includes the right to be treated as a human being with respect and fairness.

For example, the baby thrown across the room had rights, and thankfully, the nurses spoke up in defence of the child.

The Fannies hope you will do the same for the vulnerable.

You also have the right to be given information, in a way that you can understand. If you don't, then find a nice 'Fanny' or a nice 'Schlong' who can explain things to you.

Today, you have choices.

Pull the Fanny finger if you don't want to be used as a training instrument for junior doctors.

Masturbation Competition for Men

Did you know that you can go to a "Slap-Ya-Monkey-athon?"

It is held in San Francisco, and one lucky schlong held the record for the longest custard chuck (nine hours and fifty-eight minutes).

As the 'cock' struck the hour, the spectators ducked for cover.

'Worn Out Willy' used sexual aids to help him on his journey. The Fannies imagined that his schlong must have resembled a shrivelled up, overcooked schnitzel at the finale.

Let the Fannies know your record.

The Oldest Virgin

Did you know that the oldest virgin was called Miss Clara Meadmore?

Clara never got the chance to cry out in passion,

Come to me my love, because I 'mead' you some 'more.'

The Fannies don't know, if she ever sought passion through her 'Fanny fingers… she just wasn't telling.

Perhaps the closest thing that came to the smell of fish for her was actually fish!

The only cherry that popped in Clara was the cherry tart she popped in her mouth at afternoon tea.

Clara stated at one hundred and eight that she was just too busy for any of that 'argy bargy.'

The Fannies say, "good on you Clara for staying 'gloop free!'

The World's Biggest Testicles

Did you know that the world's biggest scrotum was owned by Wesley Warren Jr?

He carried around a whopping sixty kilograms (132.5 lbs) of weight between his legs.

The Fannies think he could have got a scooter to ride them around.

He suffered from a condition called Scrotal Elephantiasis. After an unsuccessful fundraising mission to help get them lopped off, poor old Warren thought he was stuck with the enormous 'hairy onions' for the rest of his life.

A kind surgeon (see, there are some good ones) became aware of poor Warren's plight and lopped them off for free.

This relieved Warren of his 'ten stone boulders', and rumour has it they required a forklift to take them away to the hospital incinerator.

Warren initially got his life back on track, but sadly, soon afterwards he passed away. Rest in peace, Warren.

He didn't stand a cat in hell's chance of being able to examine his ample ball bags for any kind of lumps and bumps.

The Fannies would like you men to know the importance of giving your 'sweaty nads' a gentle feel every now and again.

If you don't like the thought of giving them a squeeze, then another tried and trusted method is to get your other half to feel them up for you.

The word scrotum has taken on many different and colourful synonyms over the years.

Here are just a few to tickle your nether regions:
- Fruity pebbles
- Coin purse
- Slouch pouch
- Crown jewels
- Nutmeat
- Skin hat

The Fannies could go on and on… can you think of anymore? If you do, let them know.

The World Biggest Natural Breasts

The world's biggest natural breasts are owned by Annie Hawkins Turner, who wears a size fifty-two L bra.

Annie states that her record-breaking bazookas began to develop at age nine, and luckily for her, they eventually slowed down.

Annie didn't want to mess with nature and get them lopped off like Wesley Warren's large hairy onions. Instead, she embraced her humongous fun bags.

It must be such a palaver for her to examine those sweater stretchers. Perhaps she gets her other half to assist, squeezing her like a lemon, while checking for lumps and bumps.

(If you find any of your own, please see your doctor).

The Fannies would like you to know that you don't have to suffer like Annie.

Fanny suffered with her own oversized melons, and one day she decided she had had enough of the sweat rashes, debilitating back pain, chronic headaches, and breathlessness.

The Fannies recommend you seek out a well-established plastic surgeon and get them moulded into perkier proportions. Make sure you have good anaesthetist on hand, too, because you will want to be really asleep, unlike Mrs Minge later on in this book.

The Fanny Heavyweight

Tatiata Kozhevnikova from Russia holds the world record for the strongest vagina.

She hated her weak droop after childbirth, so started 'weight lifting' between her legs.

The Fannies wondered, with all the Fannies in the world, how this record was even achieved? No one has ever telephoned them, asking to measure the strength of their saloon doors!

Tatiata is worth her weight in Fanny gold. She even made it into *The Guinness Book of World Records*.

The judges must have fought over who was going to go down on her to take the recordings.

Tatiata's twat's strength is probably akin to that of a bicycle rack. When riding Tatiata, or anyone else for that matter, one mustn't forget to wear a helmet.

This should be the law.

Bullying - Is This Happening to You?

The Fannies have both been bullied, and there is no making light of this.

Its effects can be soul destroying.

Bullying causes all sorts of devastating symptoms:

- Anxiety
- Depression
- Insomnia
- Social isolation
- Hopelessness and thoughts of suicide.

It is believed that eighty per cent of suicides may be attributed to bullying.

Interestingly, the number one reason for being bullied is because of attitudes towards another's appearance.

The Fannies find that odd, because their bullies were no bloody oil paintings.

If you also feel socially excluded, you may have been bullied. This is where you are left out of communication and social events.

The silent treatment is also a nasty form of bullying.

It is a common tactic used by narcissists to gain control over a person and situation. It is a cruel and effective method of mind control, which can lead the victim down a pathway to mental illness.

Are you a cowardly bully?

If you are one; did you know that you are likely to have suffered from a stressful or traumatic event in your life?

While this is no excuse, the Fannies would like you to seek professional help to deal with your own pain first, so you stop inflicting your pain onto others.

The Fannies would like to give you the opportunity to change for the better. To become that better person they know you want to be. The consequence of not doing so is that you create a situation where old age has a habit of creeping up on you.

You will end up being a lonely old bully, where your only victim left is the television set.

The Fannies believe in karma and it always comes knocking eventually.

Helpful Hints

- If you're being bullied, or know someone who is, confide in someone you trust.
- Try and speak with the sack of shit about their behaviour and how it makes you feel.
  While learning to speak up can be daunting, it can become easier if practiced with a friend first.
  For example:
  "Robin, are you aware you're a nasty fucker? I've recorded every word you've said, so try and squirm your way out of this."
  Well, maybe not that harsh!
- Be courageous and stand up for yourself and others.
  You don't want this to happen to anyone else.
- Evidence is everything, so document dates and times, who was present, and how it has affected your sense of self.

- If you can't deal with the bully amicably, make a formal complaint.
- Seek legal advice.

If all else fails, grab a fresh and smelly 'number two,' wrap it up in some rose-scented paper and tie it up with a bow. Put the neatly packaged turd into the bully's letter box.

Watch, and wait!

You Might Want To Duck For This One!

The world's biggest jet stream of spoof has been recorded at eighteen feet and nine inches. (570 cm).

A Mr Horst Schultz's 'cum' can reach the height of twelve feet and four inches. (375.92 cm).

He also holds the land ejaculatory speed record of forty-two-point five mph (68.39 kilometres).

If you see him 'cumming', you might want to duck. If he 'cums' in your eye, it would blind you in an instant.

If you are planning on doing a blow job on that stallion, Horst, please be aware; he cums out that fast, you might not have time to think about swallowing. Horst's hose is capable of doing one of two things; it may go straight down and shoot out your arse, or it will fill up your lungs and choke you to death.

Och Aye the Noo, That is a Big 'Un!

The world's largest fanny most likely belonged to a Scottish woman called Anna Swan. (1846 to 1888).

She grew at an alarming rate in her childhood, reaching a height of over seven foot (230 cm).

She met the perfect 'manny' for her 'fanny,' a chap by the name of Captain Martin Bates, (not to be confused with Master Bates...) who himself measured over seven feet tall. Capitalising on her size, she joined a freak show touring the country.

She was rich, but was she happy? Most probably not, say the two Fannies.

Poor Anna's fanny was stretched from one end of Loch Ness to the other during her labour. She birthed her own Loch Ness monster.

The sad fact is her 'Big Gin' was no help to her big baby, who was stillborn.

He weighed twenty-six pounds and measured thirty-four inches in length. The baby's head measured nineteen inches in circumference (48.26 cm).

Apparently the poor baby has a cast of itself on display today at Cleveland's Museum of Health.

This was a sad Fanny fact for the reader.

I'm a Self-Entitled, Wound-Up Git! Narcissistic Cycle of Abuse: Idolise, Devalue, Discard, Discredit and the Icing on The Cake – Destroy!

Narcissists are a completely different breed of people.

They are men and women who come from the planet Uranus, because they speak and live out of the darkness of their arses.

Literature will tell you that narcissists become fixated on fantasies such as success, control, and idyllic love, they also have something missing in their lives that other normal human beings have; something called empathy. They have no idea what it looks or feels like to understand another's feelings. Which the Fannies think is very sad.

Narcissists manipulate people and if you cease to fulfil their needs, they begin the process of tossing you out into the garbage like a used tea bag.

It is here you find yourself being put through the 'devalue' and 'discard' phases of the relationship.

There is worse to come…

They need to fill up their half-empty cup with another target, because they take no responsibility for their actions.

Their new target becomes known as the flying monkey.

Flying monkeys' are those people the narcissist uses to then discredit and destroy you, often choosing social media as that outlet. It's called bullying by proxy.

Pain and torture are what they inflict on one's life and self-esteem.

The Fannies would like you to know that you can, and must, escape.

You must also never ever look back.

Here are some of the Fannies' tips to escaping a controlling, narcissistic relationship:
- Make a plan – and stick to it.
- Have a close friend in whom you can confide (not one of their friends).
- Set a date to leave and stick to it.
- Get your finances in order. Open your own secret bank account and build it up.
- Find somewhere to go that feels safe and secure. Only telling people you can trust.
- Plan on leaving when the demon is away from the house.
- Give the 'two fingered Fanny salute' as you walk out of the door, and never look back.
- Perhaps leave a parting gift in their letter box. You know what that gift is by now!

If you have the courage to tell your narcissist that you are leaving, you may have to put up with fake tears and snot.

They may then employ a tactic known as 'hoovering,' where they give you lots of fresh empty promises. If you feel you should stay and give it another go, ask yourself one question;

"Did they keep the last promise they made to me?"

"Did they fuck?"

Even worse still. You may find yourself on the end of their 'wolf in sheep's clothing' wrath.

So whatever you do, stay safe and still leave! Then get yourself a decent therapist to help you come to terms with the nightmare you found yourself in, through no fault of your own.

Finally, you may need to notify the police, because sometimes they have the habit of turning really nasty and may even stalk you.

There is no cure for what ails those mind fucks!

The Fannies would like to give you one of their own red flag moments:

If the person you are with is nice to you, but bloody rude to the waiter, you are not with a good person, end of story.

So let them pay for your dinner, while you apologise to the waiter for their behaviour, and run as fast as you can in the opposite direction.

A Nursing Station Tale or Two

Tale 12
How to Fertilise Your Garden – The Natural Way

Once upon a time…

Mary rushed into the nurse's station. She was unusually late, and the nurses had already started their morning report.

She put her head on the desk and started to bang it against the wood. Fanny and her colleagues looked on perplexed.

Fanny stopped the report before Mary knocked herself out, asking her what was wrong.

Mary proceeded to tell her colleagues what had happened.

Mary's Father was a minister in their local town. He was well respected and worked hard for the community.

He was on call day and night, and Mary felt it was to his detriment. She was always telling him to slow down.

Her father, Father Godwin, as he was known, looked exhausted; so much so that Mary and her family noticed a change in his behaviour.

He just couldn't say no, and was so overwhelmed, he had become miserable.

He was running on empty, poor sleep, poor appetite, and in desperate need of a rest.

Mary felt she had to come to his rescue.

Now, nurses are known for their secret stashes of un-prescribed goodies.

What is in these stashes? you ask.

The best first aid kits in the country!

One of the Fannies used to work with a nurse whose car boot was a whole A&E department. Her colleagues thought that accidents went looking for her, because she was always coming to work with tales of her 'life saving' escapades.

So what was in that first aid kit?
- Sleeping pills, for night shift insomnia
- Antibiotics, just in case of a 'puss' emergency
- Rolls of Plaster of Paris, just in case of a broken bone.

Fanny would like you to know that she broke her husband's 'bone' one evening.

However, that's a tale for another day!

Fanny also used her Plaster of Paris for the making of crafts, which she sold at the local shop.

Using a roll of that plaster and a cardboard vomit bowl, Fanny once made a 'Schlong Hat' for her colleague, Dick. He still treasures it to this very day.

Mary's Dad was exhausted, so she dug deep into her stash and pulled out a 'special little something' to help him relax.

He was initially reluctant, because he hadn't taken medication before, but he trusted his daughter; she would never let anything awful happen to him.

Chugging down a big glass of water, he swallowed a couple of the little pink pills and then put himself to bed.

Now, with Father 'their father' tucked up safe and sound, Mary and her mother settled down for a night in front of the television.

It wasn't too long before the phone rang; it was the local police.

They said that they had received a call from someone who had seemed very upset. They reported a naked man wandering the streets, and her father fitted the description.

Mary then checked the bedroom and screamed,

"OH, MY FUCKING GOD IN HEAVEN…!"

After a search of the town, they eventually found him in a parishioner's garden. He was squatting down quite happily over her dahlias. He looked up at Mary, smiled and bewilderingly asked,

"Have you got some toilet paper, dear?"

115

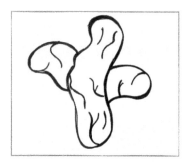

Mary's father needed a few days to recover and Fanny heard that the parishioner's dahlias had come first place in the local flower competition.

Tale 13
It's Not Only Goldfish That Get Flushed!

Fanny woke up and felt a familiar heaviness welling up inside.

Her gut instinct told her exactly what was happening, the gut being so much louder than her hopeful mind. An instinct she came to trust more as her life evolved.

Fanny just knew…

There was no physical pain, just a familiar sense of impending doom.

She got up quietly and went to the bathroom. As she sat down on the cold toilet seat, her body confirmed her instinct as it began to rapidly expel the results of her pregnancy.

As she sat there, numb, she recalled memories of similar experiences, not her own.

During her nursing career, she had tended to many previously hopeful parents, who had presented to A&E with the familiar look of shock and denial.

Fanny got up, but suddenly felt dizzy and slid to the floor. Kneeling before the toilet, plunging her hands deep into the bloodied water, she proceeded to frantically search for any sign of what was left of her unborn child.

She screamed out to Gordon to get a bucket and utensil.

Together, they ladled out what they could, while she continued to cry,

"Find my baby."

Fanny was distraught, as she knew the rapid expulsion had most likely flushed away some of the contents of her womb. Other than clots, there was nothing to be found.

Later, when she had returned home from the hospital, they buried the contents of the bucket, and planted a tree.

Over the years, Gordon and Fanny planted many such trees on their property until one day, they got to plant a placenta. That tree would flourish and blossom for years to come.

What you don't know, dear reader, is this; Fanny's grief was compounded by the grief of other women in similar situations. She had emptied many miscarriages into the 'miscarriage bucket,' a metal bucket labelled exactly that way, and for that exact purpose.

She never once took a peek as she pressed the button to flush its contents down the sluice.

She just couldn't bring herself to do it.

One day, her nursing colleague did take a look. She told Fanny she had seen a perfectly-formed foetus beneath all the blood and clots.

The experience gave her nightmares for months.

The Fannies want to honour your loss and voice their disgust at this old-fashioned and insensitive practice.

It is a practice that remains in some cultures, even today.

Whether or not you get to meet your baby, you felt it growing inside you, and that is enough to honour the experience, whether or not you got to hold your child.

Tale 14
A Mooving Love Story

Fanny's friend, Daisy, was unusually late for work, and Fanny was starting to get worried.

All of a sudden, Daisy rushed into the nurses' station. She had been crying, so Fanny asked what was wrong.

Daisy told Fanny that she had been doing her dishes while looking out of her kitchen bay window.

She was enjoying the view of her garden and watching the cows graze on her dairy farm. She said life felt so perfect... but not for long!

Daisy thought she saw something from the corner of her eye. (Those 'corner of the eye' moments, do require further investigation!)

She took herself outside to get a closer look and observed her farm hand tying a calf up against the fence. She thought that was an odd thing to do.

She then watched him stroke his hands up and down the calf's back, and then go on to seductively slap its rump. He proceeded to unzip his trousers and the rest is bestiality history.

The farmhand no longer works for Daisy and the calf was untied and mooved safely away from any further harm.

This was a 'vealy' disturbing tale now wasn't it?!

Tale 15
'Jump yer Bastard!'

Once upon a time… Fanny moved to the seaside.

She thought living in a small town would be relaxing, but she soon found herself being rostered shifts that no one else wanted.

Her attempts at starting a social life were flushed down the sluice with the rest of the of piss and poop, however Fanny chose to stay optimistic.

Little did she know that, one day, she would be living the life of Riley, meet the other Fanny, and write a book about their lives.

Fanny was working in an operating theatre, where she made the most incredible friends.

Downtime at the nurses' station was rare.

Nurses were banned from using the Internet and cell phones, and they likened that to drug withdrawal.

A surgeon who worked there was nicknamed 'The Lamppost'. His front teeth clambered out of his mouth like elephant tusks. Lamppost was an unfortunate-looking man.

He would draw the mucous back into his throat whenever he spoke, and it reminded Fanny of someone sucking on a straw.

"Just look at him," said Rita. "That poor man has got a face like a slapped arse, and I bet his weaner is as skinny as the inside of a ball point pen. Would you let that creature dip its nib into your ink, Fanny?"

"Rita, that's so cruel!" laughed Fanny. "Stop before I piss my pants."

Rita was Fanny's good friend. Each time they worked together, she would offer Fanny a spare pair of knickers, for her Niagara moments.

The thing about nurses is this; they have a black sense of humour and this survival tactic gets them through the toughest of times.

Rita's philosophy was, 'What people say about me is none of my business Fanny, so I really don't give a shit. We both know that it's Picket Fence over there that gets us into trouble'.

Rita and Fanny had been pulled up many times about their non-stop banter. It was always after the Lamppost had been working, and Rita felt he deserved a bit of stick back.

Rita and Fanny had a couple of hours to spare before the next patient arrived.

Their one and only patient was out for the count. They kept topping him up with sleeping juice, so he wouldn't disturb them as they chatted.

Rita was a glamorous woman in her mid-fifties. She had perfectly polished fingernails, even though that was banned. She had rings on every finger (also banned), and beautiful red coloured hair (banned). Rita was a rebel, and Fanny loved her. Rita always had a story to tell and she was desperate to tell Fanny about her recent cruise to Hawaii.

She sat back and put her feet up on the desk, while Fanny did the same.

"Hurry up and tell me what happened, Rita; my bladder's bursting at the seams."

So Rita began.

"Don't get me wrong, Fanny, I love that husband of mine, but on this trip he made such a commotion I still haven't quite forgiven him. What he did was so bloody embarrassing. I'm still trying to block it from my memory."

Fanny was so enthralled that she took the phone off the hook.

"Oh, my God, what on earth did he do?"

Rita repositioned her rump on the swivel chair and continued telling her tale.

"Well, it's a known fact, Fanny, that my Terry fucking hates flying. The last time we went on a plane, he puked up the whole way and had one of his panic attacks. He kept ringing the bell, telling the stewardess the plane was about to crash.

"He asked; 'Who's gonna find me at the bottom of this great big sodding ocean, Miss?'

"He then pulled the life jacket from under his seat, Fanny,

and it took all my effort to stop him from putting it on and blowing the whistle."

Rita took a deep breath and continued.

"I had one of my 'mother's little helpers,' so I slammed a couple of those down his throat. It knocked him out for the rest of the trip, otherwise I think they would have diverted the plane to an island and just left him there."

Fanny and Rita laughed out loud.

"But this was a cruise. What on earth could go wrong?" asked Fanny.

Rita replied, rolling her eyes,

"Fucking everything."

Fanny quickly ran to the loo, then got them both a cuppa, and Rita carried on.

"Because of his fear of flying, I agreed to go on a cruise, as Terry said he would feel much safer on the ocean. Little did I know, he had it all figured out.

"He mentioned he had purchased his own life jacket. When I watched him pack, I really thought nothing of it. I knew the ship had their own lifejackets, but if it helped him relax, I was happy.

"I was so excited for this holiday Fanny... I was ready to put on my bathing suit and relax by the pool with a fag and a margarita."

"Oh, that sounds lovely," said Fanny, "so what happened next?"

"Well, we had just spent our first night on board after a fabulous day by the pool. Terry had been parading around in his black speedos, feeling like he'd won the lottery. He thought he looked gorgeous, but he didn't notice that his big beer gut made him look as though he was butt naked."

Rita and Fanny both laughed.

"The next day the weather took a turn for the worse. The sky turned grey and the wind started howling. The captain said we were passing through a small storm and instructed we stay in our cabins. The waves began curling over the railings, leaving a fine mist of foam on the deck. I wasn't worried at all, but each time the boat rocked and rolled, so did Terry's anxiety. His face went whiter by the minute."

"Oh no," laughed Fanny. "Did he have another of his panic attacks?"

"No, Fanny, it was much worse than that. He was screaming at me, 'We are going to capsize, Rita. We are all going to die. We will be dragged down with this fuckin' Titanic to the bottom of the sea and be eaten by sharks. We are all going to die, love!'"

Fanny was crying by this stage, wiping the tears from her face, hoping it wasn't time for another Niagara moment.

"For crying out loud Fanny, he was in a right state. I felt like throwing him overboard myself. I took him to the bar for a stiff drink, but he still carried on. Everyone around us thought he was joking, but I knew he wasn't. They all stood there and laughed. I had just about had a gutsful, so I told him to go back to the cabin and have a lie down."

Fanny was speechless as Rita went on…

"It's what he did next that really takes the ginger biscuit, Fanny. I went looking for him and couldn't find the silly sod anywhere. I wondered if someone else had thrown him overboard to shut him up, so I went back to the bar to look for him, and there he was, in all his glory. What stood in front of me has scarred me for life," Rita sighed, then continued.

"Terry was standing there with his new life jacket on. But it wasn't a normal life jacket, it was a full bloody blow-up suit that floats on the water. It covered him from head to toe, and even had a blow-up helmet. He'd already inflated both and stood there like some great big floaty old twat. He also had this big fuckin' buoy sat on top of his beer gut."

Rita started laughing as hard as Fanny, who was falling off her chair and onto her fanny by this point.

It was definitely Niagara time for them both.

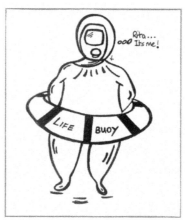

"OMG, Rita, I'm dying," cried Fanny, tears streaming down her face.

They both took turns nipping to the loo, and once fanny got back, Rita continued;

"The children thought he was an act, and they all started clapping. It was then I heard a familiar squeak coming from his helmet, and I realised it was that stupid man. I could barely make out what he was saying, Fanny, so I shouted, 'Take your fucking helmet off, you stupid twat…'

Terry then took off his helmet, and calmly said, 'Rita, if the ship capsizes, my suit has internal heating that will keep me warm as I swim to shore. I'm prepared for the worst, love. Isn't that great?'

"He wasn't prepared for my reply, Fanny… So, where's my fucking suit, Terry? You know, Terry, the woman you've been married to for thirty years?"

"He just stood there and said nothing. I clipped him across the earhole, because all he bloody cared about was himself, he didn't give a shit about me and the thought of buying me one hadn't crossed his mind."

Lamppost walked up to the nurses' station and by then it was too late for them to compose themselves.

Funnily enough, though, he was grinning like a buck-toothed Cheshire Cat.

He had overheard the entire story. He looked straight at Rita, slurping,

"I would have bought you a life jacket, Rita."

The three of them were absolutely hysterical. So much so, that they woke up their patient.

Following this incident they all came to an understanding, and the nurses' station became its own 'life jacket' for doctors and nurses alike.

Lamppost went on to marry one of Rita's nursing friends, with Rita even babysitting for their 'little pickets.'

Tale 16:
The Lifeless Lover

Once upon a time…many years ago,
In a hospital covered in white crispy snow,
An assistant called Babs, poked Fanny and said,
"Have you heard of the rumour, that's being widespread?"

"Have I heard what?" answered Fanny, intrigued,
Babs then replied, "Fanny, it's about Mrs Seed.
Her marriage is broken, all she does is cry,
When I tell you what's happened, you'll understand why!"

"So poor Mrs Seed, well, she needed a smear,
So she went to the nurse to get the all clear.
"Come back in a week, I'm sure you're okay,"
Instructed the nurse, sending the specimen away.

Then after two days, the GP, he rang,
"You need to come in now," he urgently sang.
"Oh dear," she thought, "This is really a worry,"
She put on her coat and went down in a hurry.

When on her arrival, she went to his room,
A young copper was waiting, his face full of gloom.
They asked that she sit, and the questions began,
Mrs Seed tried to answer, the best that she can.

.

"Now can you recall your last 'humping' with Rex?"
Mrs Seed replied, "Yes, dear, we always have sex."
The cop said "Dear lady, I'm sorry to say,
I'm now going to spoil your lovely spring day."

"Mrs Seed, I despair, I don't want to cause trouble,
But I need to investigate this case on the double."
Mrs Seed then felt faint, and laid down on the bed,
"It will all be okay love," her dear GP said.

The policeman went on, "I now have your results,"
Mrs Seed listened eagerly to the consult.
"Your smear test is back, and the report, it read,
What was found in your fanny, has come from the dead."

Now, Rex was well known, in the village he resided,
Working with families, where funerals were decided.
He drove a black car, also known as a hearse,
Rex was now busted, his secret perverse.

The GP and PC, put two and two together,
Rex was having sex, with those a bit under the weather!
"Oh, my dear God, he's been fucking a stiff,"
"You're right, Mrs Seed, it was old Mr Cliff."

"I'll have to arrest Rex", then said the young Bobby,
"We can't have him shagging the stiffs as a hobby."
Rex got fifteen years, the dirty old bugger,
Mrs Seed soon moved on and hooked up with his brother.

Tale 17:
A Hole In One

Once upon a time...

In a land far away, where the green hills rolled on forever, a place where the sun was so bright, it cracked the lenses on Fanny's five-dollar sunglasses, a young, worn out Fanny started her chaotic shift at the local A&E.

She remembers as if it was yesterday.

In charge of that shift was a nurse manager-whose face reminded Fanny of a battered piece of overcooked cod.

Fanny absolutely hated her... and she also hated Fanny.

Fanny was targeted on a daily basis.

"Fanny this, Fanny that, Fanny, you can't do anything bloody right!" she would scream.

Battered Cod would scream, demean, and belittle her so much, that Fanny had to hand her surgical scissors to a colleague, just in case she felt homicidal.

One day, Battered Cod ordered Fanny to assist a newly graduated doctor.

Fanny looked forward to some time away from the fishy fucker.

"Get your arse down to the room and help Dr Simon with his examination," Cod demanded.

Fanny muttered something to the effect of,

"Get me my scissors so I can scrape off your fishy scales and slowly gut you."

Fanny then watched as Battered Cod's wobbly arse, waddled off down the corridor. Her greasy fish and chip shop hair was scraped into a scruffy ponytail and she wore the thickest jam jar glasses you've ever seen.

Fanny thinks she probably brushed her teeth with tartare sauce, shit curry sauce out of her arse, and menstruated ketchup into her knickers. Her breath even had the smell of a pickled egg.

Fanny would like you to know that she isn't a nasty bully, but she was eaten alive by this woman.

This is Fanny's way of letting off steam.

Now, going back to the story; Fanny arrived at the examination room and could hear the cries of pain coming from within. She entered the room to investigate.

"That's it, Mrs Sp… Sp… Sp… Spread. Just open your legs a little w… w… w… wider, so I can get a really good l… l… l… look," stuttered the young doctor.

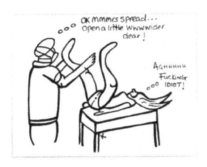

Simple Simon, as he was known, was right out of med school. He still had school yard pimples on his forehead and a chin that needed a good pussy squeeze.

His unkemptness was evident in his un-ironed trousers and sweat patches under the arms of his shirt. He smelled like Fanny's teenage son after a game of football.

Once she left a subtle can of deodorant in his locker, but it made no difference.

"Do you need a hand, Simon?" Fanny asked, while pinching her nose shut.

Mrs Spread was lying spread eagled, leaving nothing to the imagination.

She was groaning in pure agony. Fanny knew that catheters could be a little uncomfortable, but no worse than that.

What the hell is going on here? Fanny wondered.

Simple Simon had her legs open so wide that Fanny worried she was at risk of a hip dislocation.

She wondered if he thought his patient was a ballet dancer, testing her out to see if she could do the splits.

"No help needed here, thanks F… F… F… Fanny," Simon answered, "I've found the right hole, and I'm waiting for urine to flow," he said excitedly.

Still concerned, Fanny went in for a closer look.

"Aghhh! I feel like I'm splitting in half!" screamed Mrs Spread.

Simon continued his poking, and he wasn't that gentle, either. Fanny imagined him poking his girlfriend, and thought she may need to give him some 'go gently' education.

Fanny then realised why Mrs Spread was screaming.

"Simon, stop what you are doing, and take that out immediately!"

Fanny pushed him away from Mrs Spread with so much force, he nearly lost his footing.

Simon wasn't happy, and neither was Mrs Spread's clitoris. It had swelled up to the size of a satsuma.

"For fuck's sake, Simon," whispered Fanny. "Did they not teach you anything about female anatomy in med school?"

Simon looked at Fanny horrified; his cheeks turned as red as Cod's ketchup. He quickly stepped back to let Fanny catheterise the correct hole and Mrs Spread soon settled down.

Simon then apologised to both of them and shuffled out of the room, doing the walk of shame.

Fanny was left to fix Mrs Spread's munched up clitoris, and unfortunately, it was more traumatised than at first thought. It had taken such a bashing, Fanny had to apply an ice pack, because Mrs Spread's 'satsuma,' had become the size of a blood orange.

Later that day, Fanny tracked Simon down. She got out a pen and paper, and gave him an anatomy lesson.

If you need one of your own, please read the following:
Top bit = clitoris (requires gentle stimulation)
Middle hole = Urethra (piss pot)
Bottom hole = vagina (requires quality over quantity)
Bum hole = Bum hole (lube if you stick things up it)

Simple Simon came to work the next day and found another gift in his locker. He found an anonymous, hand-written poem:

Simple Simon met his patient,
For her it wasn't fair,
Said Simple Simon to his patient,
"What's going on d... d... d... down there?"

Said the patient, to Simple Simon,
"I hope you know what you're doing,
I have three holes for I'm a woman,
They're for peeing, pooping, and screwing."

Says the patient to Simple Simon,
"Keep away from my place of pleasure,"
Says Simple Simon to the patient,
"I'm only catching your urine to m… m… m… measure."

Says Simple Simon to his patient,
"I'm getting so confused,"
Says Simple Simon to his patient,
"W… w… w… which hole do I use?"

The patient screamed to Simple Simon,
"I'm traumatised for ever."
Says the patient to Simple Simon,
"You've destroyed my satsuma's pleasure."

Says Simple Simon to his patient,
"I'm sorry for your pain,"
Says simple Simon to his patient,
"I've gone back to m… m… m… med school again."

Fanny Fact:
Getting to Know One's Clitoris

While middle age presents its challenges: spaniel ears, Niagara moments, pegged-up faces and sagging tree of life tattoos – did you know that after menopause, the clitoris grows two-and-a-half times larger? The Fannies have never measured their pleasure plates the way that men measure their penises.

Why do they do that?

It's not about the size, it's about the quality, after all.

Three cheers for quality, ladies and gentlemen.

The clitoris is actually a miniature penis, and is only partially visible to the naked eye (as you will know, if you have gone down there to get a closer look).

The clitoris is actually around four inches long and three quarters of it is tucked up inside. So ladies, we have our very own little schlong to play with.

It's a known fact that fifty to seventy-five percent of women who have climaxes need to have their 'satsumas' stimulated by sensual touch.

If your lover is only concerned about their own finale, then wait until the selfish sack of shit falls asleep and get busy on yourself.

Tale 18:
Ode to the Cleaners

Once upon a time…

Close to retiring, was dear old Sadie,
Known as the gossiping, but kind cleaning lady.
She swept her way round, all the wooden ward floors,
Whilst eavesdropping in on those half-closing doors.

Everyone loved her vivacious demeanour,
For forty odd years, she had been their dear cleaner.
But her outside life, was a 'punching bag' tale,
Poor Sadie, was paired with a cowardly male.

She loved the Royal family, that gave her an out,
From the regular kicking's, and knockings about.
For Queen and country, she'd lie back and think.
As he attacked her undercarriage, after a drink.

Many children were birthed, that she gave lots of love,
All because she believed in the heaven above.
She stayed with that pig, all because of her vows,
Hiding her bruises from raised up eyebrows.

Fanny wished she could throw the pig into the sluice,
With the rest of the piss, and its shitty old juice.
But Sadie stayed with him, until life was done,
Living with a bastard, that thought he had won.

Fanny hopes dearly, when reading this tale,
That if this is you, common sense will prevail.
Reach out and get help, yes! You don't need to stay,
So fuck off to all who behave in this way.

Then Sadie told Fanny, karma knocked at the door,
When he found himself cuffed, on the living room floor.
He'd been caught stealing knickers, off ladies lines,
While peeking in windows, and half open blinds.

Now Sadie's safe place was the postnatal ward,
One day she observed some marital discord.
A visiting father, who staggered in drunk,
The drunken pig's smell, was much worse than a skunk.

The visit to his wife was of vicious intent,
To harm the new mother, he was hellbent.
He took the new born from her arms, to his cot,
Whispering sweet nothings, into her bed he got.

Sadie ran up, and grabbed him by the throat,
Kicking his arse, like an old Billy goat.
The bastard thrown out, by security's Steven,
For Sadie it felt like she was getting even.

Ode to the cleaners, we love you so much,
Your pure dedication, and handholding touch.
You all work so hard and we want you to know,
The Fannies salute you, may your happiness grow.

Tale 19:
The Fishmongers Market

Once upon a summertime…

Where the hot sun sparkled over the ocean, and the grapes grew ripe and plentiful, Fanny found her work life had dramatically improved, which included the bliss of every weekend off.

Gone were the days that her bladder extended to the size of a beach ball, because she was denied the basic human right to urinate.

In her previous role, being spat at, sworn at, kicked and punched, while having human excrement thrown at her, had become the norm. So it felt extremely strange to leave work in a uniform that didn't smell and look like a public toilet.

She had also stopped prising her tired eyes open with match sticks, and was glad she had said her final goodbye to the Battered Cod.

Fanny almost felt guilty about her newfound luxury. That's not to say that her new life was a bed of roses, but as change is the only constant in life, she embraced it with open arms.

Wherever she went, she still met the 'old school doctors,' those who treated nurses like something stuck to the bottom of their shoes.

Nurses were the lowest of the low at a time when ranking was everything.

As a junior nurse, Fanny can't remember a single day where she wasn't abused in some way, shape or form.

One particular experience has often played on Fanny's mind.

"Nurse Fanny, come over here. Are you fucking stupid? I told you not to let this child's mother into theatre, why are you so disobedient?"

Dr Weasel was a South African man of retirement age and he had no respect for anyone. He often voiced that he considered women to be nothing more than his personal slaves.

All the nurses prayed for him to retire.

"Do you think Dr Weasel might be retiring this month?" said Fanny's colleague.

"Did the cow actually jump over the moon?" Fanny laughed.

Dr Weasel looked a little like Santa, but he was no bloody Santa at all.

He was a fat bastard, with a big, white beard, and his voice was an aggressive trombone. Fanny disliked him with a vengeance, but she wasn't scared of him, like some of the other nurses.

She had just done a double shift, and was functioning on little sleep, when he blasted his trombone in front of everyone.

For Fanny, it was the straw that broke the camel's back!

She stuck her Fanny fingers in the air and shouted back, "Shut the fuck up, you shrivelled dick Santa!"

Everyone stood there frozen, eyes popping and mouths agape, while Santa went the same shade as his suit.

The whole room looked like it wanted to break out into applause. However, Dr Weasel's clenched fists gave a signal that this probably wasn't the right time.

He turned on his heels and stormed off.

From that day on, he avoided Fanny like the plague and he never spoke to her again.

She is afraid that others were not so lucky. For Fanny, it was one of the most liberating moments of her nursing career.

She was now on Santa's naughty list, and she didn't give

an elf's arse about it.

Bizarrely, Dr Weasel eventually got his opportunity to shine. Some said he even saved the day.

It was colonoscopy day, and there were a dozen bum holes to photograph and sweep clean. The attending anaesthetist was Dr Weasel.

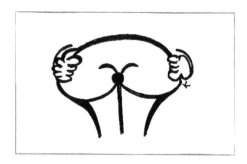

The surgeon was a small, balding man called Dr Small Man Syndrome.

Dr Syndrome was also an old school narcissist. Oddly, he had women dropping at his feet, and Fanny could never figure out what women saw in him. Perhaps it was the 'big man no dick,' 'small man all dick' phenomenon.

The theatre had been prepared and Dr Weasel was busy administering his special concoction of anaesthetic to Mrs Minge.

"Is she over and out, Weasel?" questioned Dr Syndrome, as he stood on his tippy toes at the other end of the bed.

"Ho ho ho - go ahead," said Dr Weasel, confirming his patient was well and truly under.

Dr Syndrome then pulled back the sheet to expose her plumber's crack.

Frowning in disgust he then bellowed,

"Don't you just hate a hairy beaver, Weasel? It smells like a fishmongers market down here."

Dr Syndrome was so close to her pubic flurry, the force of his breath almost gave her a parting.

"I'm sorry, what did you say?" said Mrs Minge, as she sat up and turned to look at the horrible little man. Mrs Minge was more awake than first thought!

In that split second of terror, Dr Weasel took hold of his reindeer reins and remedied the situation.

He administered some of 'Michael Jackson's leftover medicine' to render her unconscious. He also added a little something extra, to erase the memory from her mind.

Dr Syndrome sighed with relief, while Fanny and the others stood there, horrified.

It was a well-known fact that Weasel and Syndrome hated each other's guts, but that day changed everything. They had both just experienced the "you just saved my career" moment.

Mrs Minge never remembered what happened that day and thankfully never will.

Her colonoscopy was a success, and she left hospital with a clean poo pipe and her hairy beaver intact.

If you ever need a colonoscopy under the care of Dr Syndrome, be careful to shave, wax and douche.

You have been warned.

Fanny Fact:
Anaesthetic Bloopers

Did you know that waking up during surgery is a phenomenon called Anaesthesia Awareness?

There have been some horror stories of people waking up during surgery, as was the case with Mrs Minge.

Imagine waking up to hear that your fanny smells like a fishmongers market. It really doesn't bear thinking about, does it?

Some people need more anaesthetic than others. Smokers need thirty-three percent more because their lungs are full of soot.

For those who breathe in second-hand smoke, you also need another dose, so don't forget to tell the anaesthetist that you meet the criteria.

Beware not to use as much as Michael Jackson –"hee hee!"

Tale 20:
Ode to the Fannies

Ride a Cock Horse

So now you arrive at this part of the story,
Here is Fanny One's tale, in its tree hugging glory.
We promise you that this tale is her own,
It involves a little pony that wanted to go home.

Recovering from an operation, to right infertility,
She had struggled for years, in reproductive ability.
At home on the mend, with a very big scar,
She healed playing folk songs on her bamboo guitar.

The sun was out shining on this autumn day,
So she strolled with her husband, towards Scarborough Bay.
She took it quite slowly, feeling relatively good,
But Fanny had walked much further than she should.

Her friend and her daughter came trotting along,
Where they overheard Fanny's 'I can't walk home' song.
They stopped and they offered their pony's assistance,
So Fanny climbed on, and obeyed their persistence.

Her taxi, an overweight Shetland horse,
She grabbed onto its reins to steer its new course.
Because it was fat, it was close to the ground,
Reassuring our Fanny, she'd get home safe and sound.

They laughed at the helmet, tied under her chin,
While Fanny laughed back with her, 'I'm in pain' grin.
Her helmet bejewelled in My Little Pony pink,
Everyone giggled, while she managed a wink.

'What's going on' the horse said to itself,
'Who's on my back, weighing down my rear shelf?'
Our Fanny she wasn't that much of a jockey,
And that little fucker had now become cocky!

They left the small path and veered onto the lane,
Our Fanny atop, trying to cope with her pain.
That Shetland then bucked with all of its might,
Ran off the down the road in a galloping flight.

The rest were left standing and screaming in horror,
As he hurtled away like there was no tomorrow.
Fanny had one hand held on to her stitches,
As her arse bumped around in her padded-up britches.

As the horse turned the corner, the saddle then slipped,
And arse over tit, our dear Fanny got flipped.
Onto her head she crashed into the shingle,
And all those who witnessed, had started to mingle.

Her husband and neighbour were soon to arrive,
And astounded to find, Fanny had even survived.
The cute little helmet saved her life from the fall,
It had split into pieces, and that wasn't all...

She was unconscious.

The sound of a chopper swept over the valley,
It's first debut flight, on its life-saving rally.
When Fanny woke up, she thought she couldn't see,
"I'm blind, I'm blind, Gordon! What's happening to me?"

Her neighbour then laughed, "it's all in your mind,
Just open your eyes Fanny, you're not fucking blind!"
They flew to the A&E where Fanny was known,
While that little Shetland galloped on home.

Dozens of visitors swarmed to her bed,
On the day the pink helmet saved her from the dead.
Her husband was told that her neck was a wreck,
She needed to have a specialised check.

Gordon then whispered "I don't want a cripple,
I only married you, for your perky young nipples."
She then spun around, stared at him and said;
"You've got a small willy and you're shit in bed."

Just like her shit husband, the horse didn't care,
They just wanted rid of that fat Fanny mare.
Once Fanny got better, she eventually showed Gordon the door,
She then went online, to find her next score.

Without further ado,
I now hand you over to Fanny two…

Dying to be Skinny!

This is a tale that left Fanny two in a mess,
She had bought some green pills, from the Asian Express.
Dieting only works with disciplined precision,
So you may wish to question, Fanny two's poor decision.

"You shouldn't be doing that, Fanny," you say,
A well-balanced diet is three meals a day.
But not our dear Fanny, she was after a fix,
To get rid of the belly made by too much pick 'n' mix.

The packet said 'detox,' it made her elated,
The strange foreign words that she read were as stated;
Green tea, guarana, caffeine and garcarnia,
"My God," said our Fanny, "I'm going to be thinia."

But Fanny had no clue what all of that meant,
If the fat disappeared, it was money well spent.
She told her friend Tracey "Hey, chick, look what I've got,"
"They just came this morning, I'm taking the lot."

"Can I have some Fanny? I'm a big balloon too,
The laxatives are crap, and I've stopped shitting poo."
So Fanny gave in, and Tracey paid her the cash,
"We'll soon be thin Fanny, because of this stash."

So Fanny and Tracey started their new diet,
Their secret was solid, they both kept it quiet.
A green pill for breakfast, another for tea,
It wouldn't be long, before this turned to three.

One week turned to two, and two turned to four,
The weight soon dropped off, leaving them wanting more.
One pill went to three, and then three went to six,
At this bloody rate, they would soon look like sticks.

But then while at work, our dear Fanny felt sick,
She yelled to the doctor, "Please come here quick."
"I think I am dying, my heart won't slow down,"
Now laid on the bed in her hospital gown.

"I'm not surprised Fanny, your blood pressure's sky high,
All we need to do now, is to figure out why."
He then checked her over, and said she looked anorexic,
She then tried to sneak out, and make a quick exit.

But she was too sick, thyroid levels now double,
Her eyes had popped out, she was really in trouble.
The Doctor asked Fanny "What's the truthful tale?"
"Okay, I will tell you," she started to wail.

Then ten minutes later, while waiting outside,
Tracey soon realised, she was in for the same ride.
She dropped down and fainted, her pulse hardly there,
The doctor soon knew, to provide the same care.

She was put on a bed right next to her friend,
As the doctors and nurses continued to tend.
Her heart on a monitor, beating so fast,
Their desire to be thin was not going to last.

Then Fanny leaned over to Tracey and said;
"I'm so sorry hon, we are both nearly dead."
"Don't worry," laughed Tracey, "we had to come clean,
We soon will be well, and back on the ice cream."

"Okay," said the doc, "now you've both had a scare,
I'm still taking your arses to coronary care.
Can't you both see, you don't have to be thin,
You can still be successful with a double chin.

"I've thrown all those pills down the drain in the sluice,
The kitchen has made you both a nutritional juice.
And when you get better, we'll all make a deal,
No more green pills, just a decent sized meal."

Tale 21:
Who is Coming to Dinner?

We hope the Fannies have kept you entertained throughout their book. They have left their most shocking tale until the very end.

To get you in the mood, we would like you to sing along with them.

Dem bones, dem bones, dem dry bones... Dem bones, dem bones, dem dry bones... Dem bones, dem bones, dem dry bones...

Now shake dem skeleton bones.

Once upon a time…

In a bitterly cold and windy city by the sea, a place where the seagulls flocked like the interns, the trainees would gather in the A&E for work experience. While they were all as keen as mustard, some of the eager beavers were not aware of the term, *'there are boundaries to what one can observe'.*

Fanny had to stop many of these eager beavers from following her into the examination room, set aside for female genitalia. Having several sets of young male eyes 'copping a look' was an intrusion Fanny wouldn't tolerate. They even had the gall to complain about her locking them out.

Don't worry, ladies, Fanny stood her ground!

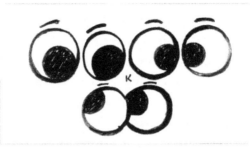

Unfortunately back then, patients' rights were limited to,

I felt I wasn't given a choice.

One of Fanny's friends had experienced several medical students fingering her expanding pussy as she dilated during labour. Thankfully, today there is a thing called 'informed consent.'

During the quiet lulls, staff would convene in the tea room for a much-deserved break. This was a safe cocoon for them to relax and banter. Sometimes Fanny would hear screams of laughter echoing down the corridor, and she would make any excuse to find out what was going on.

She has called the guilty interns in this tale, Tweedle Dee and Tweedle Fucking Dumb.

She remembers one clearly because of his skeletal stature. She remembers staring at him and thinking that it would be like having sex with a twig. A twig poking her with his boner twiglet.

His colleague was the complete opposite. Fanny remembers him as a morbidly obese, neckless man. He minced down the corridor with his flabby hips swinging from side to side.

Fanny also imagined having sex with him, and likened it to being consumed by a giant pink sweaty marshmallow. So sticky, you can't quite peel him off, no matter how hard you try. As he gets up to go to the bathroom, you start yelling,

"Haven't you forgot something? Your ball sack. It's still stuck to my thigh!"

Okay, so what Fanny is about to tell you next is really quite shocking. As shocking as when one of the doctors told her,

"When I make love to my whale of a wife, I throw flour at her first, to find the wet spot."

A horrified Fanny hoped that he had checked her wet spot wasn't gluten intolerant.

Fanny wasn't interested in either twiglet or marshmallow, but they got along famously, and it was here they began to expose their unusual lives.

This is one of their stranger tales.

Fanny imagines the invitation to their end of year class barbeque went something like this:

You are cordially invited to:
The Rib Shack,
666 Intercostal Avenue,
Marylebone,
Corpse Bay.

Tweedle Dee and Dumb said the 'chosen one' was an arrogant, self-entitled wanker. One of those who only read the cover of the text book and got one hundred percent on all of his exams. They said he never had to survive on packet noodles, because he was so well fed by Mummy's and Daddy's wallet. All they needed was to get him hammered enough to wet his appetite. An easy target by anyone's terms.

What was on the menu?

It was Cadaver!

For those of you unfamiliar with the term… it was human meat.

Fanny isn't sure if it was a Master, Mr, Ms, Miss, or Mrs.

Recipe:

- Two squeezed lemons and one finely chopped kiwifruit; the tenderiser!

There is nothing worse than chewing on Dem bones, dem bones, dem dry bones!

- Half a cup each of soy sauce, BBQ sauce, fruit chutney, and brown sugar.
- One rack of ribs sourced from your local butcher… oops excuse the blunder! One rack of ribs sourced from the medical school freezer.

Method:

- Marinate and BBQ until crisp on the outside and succulent on the inside.
- Find some self-entitled wanker to eat it.

They all watched as he tucked in and feasted on the ribs, with his lips and chin slathered in sauce. While wiping the excess sauce from his face, he drunkenly slurred,

"Mmm – Just like my mums."

The guests looked on fascinated as he continued to devour the poor cadaver.

The self-entitled mummy's boy had unsuspectingly turned cannibal.

Fanny can't confirm if he had coleslaw or a jacket potato on the side.

Many reading this today will wonder if they were 'the chosen one.'

He would be in his late fifties by now, could it be you?

Take Fanny's quiz below to see if you're also a self-entitled wanker.

This is a tale that was so unbelievable back then, and yet totally believable today.

The year and location of this story has been withheld, to protect the Cadaver, the recipient of the Cadaver, and the ethical committee of the said Medical School.

Fanny's Quiz
Are you a self-entitled wanker?

1. Do you have an excessive need for admiration? Y/N
2. Do you have a grandiose sense of self-importance? Y/N
3. Do you have a disregard for the feelings of others? Y/N
4. Are you pre-occupied with your own brilliance? Y/N
5. Do you exploit others without guilt or shame? Y/N

Scoring

Score 1 for each 'yes' answer.

1-3: You are borderline, get your shit together.

3-5: You are a self-entitled wanker.

Fanny Fact:
Cannibal Facts

There is a very good biological reason that cannibalism is off-limits.

It can make you very sick.

Did you know that there is a tribe called the Fore People in Papua New Guinea? They are renowned for serving their relatives up on a plate. Apparently, this ritual was practised until the late 1950s, and was used as a means to cleanse their spirits.

The Fore People contracted a deadly disease, the unfortunate side effect of their culinary capers. This was interestingly called the 'kuru curse.'

Those afflicted with the kuru curse presented with symptoms that saw them 'shake like a shitting dog,' as Fanny Two's grandfather would so eloquently put it. The kuru curse meant they couldn't keep anything down. Not even a cousin.

Unfortunately for many, death was the outcome.

As luck would have it, the Fore People eventually developed a genetic mutation that protected them from the disease. This meant they could still tuck into Aunty Irma Shitstirrer, Uncle Millimetre Peter, and Cousin Molly Mole, knowing they were safe to do so.

Goodbye from the Fannies

It's time to say goodbye, dear reader...

The Fannies hoped you enjoyed the ride... they certainly did!

They hope the therapy they gained from writing this book has provided you with some therapy of your own. Perhaps a sense of justice for a health system that at one time may have let you down.

The Fannies are sorry they weren't there to catch you when you fell, or your baby, for that matter.

Their nursing tales have seen them mix with the good, the bad, and the extremely ugly side of a nurse's career. However, they prefer to remember the good times and the good people.

If you are one of the good people, they salute and thank you. In spreading your own magic fairy dust of kindness, you are making the world a better place, for all the 'little pickets' being born today.

As for the bad people, that's a whole different fucking story.

The two Fannies are big believers in the fact that you reap what you sow.

So, now you know how to do the Fanny fingered salute, let's all give 'two fingers' to those who treat others like pieces of dog turd.

The Fannies' nursing careers have taken them around the world and, although fulfilling, chaotic and at times disturbing, it has also been bloody exhausting work.

Their commitment to continuing to work with buggered backs and overextended bladders has prevailed. In spite of the imbalance in what, back then, was an incredibly self-entitled hierarchal system.

So committed were they that Fanny One, was once knocked off her bike on the way to work. She then limped into the A&E, while still holding what was left of her bike. She patched up her lumps, bumps and grazes, and completed her shift.

Fanny Two once had a car accident, suffering a concussion. She was told to come to work regardless, and so she climbed off the ambulance stretcher and did.

The Fannies aren't expecting an Oscar; it was just how things were back then.

Their desire for a kind and caring world has never waned. Their ultimate dream is to spread laughter and joy around a world that has become dominated by doom and gloom… and narcissists.

You may have been shocked by what you have read, but the Fannies felt writing the truth was their 'duty of care,' while exposing the rotten and guilty parties.

Acknowledging the treasures of this world is just as important to them, these being the orderlies, the cleaners, 'Turn the Boat Back Mike,' and 'Father their Father,' who found himself in a very embarrassing predicament.

The Fannies are now far too old and wise for all that hospital palaver. They have done their time and earned a rest.

Now they want to lie on a sun chair, with a Pina Colada in one hand and a published *The Tales of the Two Fannies* book in the other. While the silky ocean waves wash over their worn out bunion-covered feet, they watch Harold wash ashore in his blow-up suit.

If you love this book, you will love the next one, as it is about the Fannies' own crazy lives outside the hospital doors.

It starts something like this...

Once upon a time, on a warm spring day, Fanny was sitting on her bathroom floor, looking into a mirror, as she waxed her 'closed for winter' overgrown fanny. All of a sudden...

The End

Explanation of Certain Words and Colloquialisms.

A&E - Accident and Emergency - aka ED. A place where lots of people go with paper cuts because their GPs are too busy to see them. Or a place to go where your life is saved, or not!

Anaphylactic Shock- Refers to someone with a severe, life-threatening allergic reaction, like someone who has been in contact with a bee sting or a narcissist.

Argy Bargy – Argument, fight, spat, have a crack at someone.

Big Gin – Tunnel of love, vagina. The size of the tunnel depends on how many wee tots have come through its channel.

Boulders – Wesley Warren's scrotal sack.

Breasts – Referred to in this book as fun bags, sweater stretchers, spaniel's ears, bazookas and oversized melons.

Catatonics – Those of a rigid and mental unresponsiveness. They usually present with 'wide open googly eyes' that don't blink.

Cat in hell's chance – No bloody chance!

Catheterisation – A tube put up the *middle hole* so you can pee.

Charge Nurse - Often a person whose power has gone to their head, turning them into a nasty fucker, who rosters you on twelve hour shifts for two weeks, with one day off.

Chlamydia - A common sexually transmitted infection that makes your nether regions drip like a fucked fridge. Treated with common antibiotics that can be found in any 'Fannies' first aid kit.'

Chum – A type of dog food.

Colonoscopy - A procedure in which a hose pipe is inserted into one's star fish (anus) in order to examine the colon for abnormalities. Don't worry; they put you to sleep. Well, usually!

Colostomy Bag – A shit catcher, that protrudes out of your stomach.

Copping a look - 'Copping a look,' is in the same basket as 'Copping a feel'. It is usually performed by some pervert at work or at the pub. An example would be a male, speaking to a female's chest instead of her face.

Cum – A slang word for 'ejaculation gloop,' or your daily protein shot!

Custard Chuck - Term for masturbation's ejaculatory ending.

CV – 'Curriculum Vitae.' A superficial document that is usually full of shit. Your CV front page should provide the following; 'This potential employee is not a narcissist, psychopath or sociopath'.

Drop off the twig – Pop your clogs.

ECG – Electrocardiogram. A test that detects if you are alive or not.

Episiotomy – A surgical cut, made at the opening of the vagina during childbirth. It usually leaves the old fanny looking like a munched-up piece of lettuce.

Evacuated – Medicine that makes the poo pipe go into overdrive.

Fanny Flaps – A derogatory word for a female's 'Labia Majora.' Also known as the 'vaginal lips', or 'piss flaps'.

The Fanny Finger explained:
(Resembles the middle fingered "fuck off salute.")

- Press your index and middle finger together,
- Do a half circle of both fingers until the base of your two fingers are facing you,
- The quicker you do it, the speedier the message to the person on the receiving end of your Fanny fingers.

Fanny Curtains – Also a derogatory term for the' Labia Majora' or 'vaginal lips.'

Filling her knickers – Shitting your pants.

Full English – A cooked breakfast, comprising of a big banger and a couple of fried eggs, beans, and copious cups of Niagara-forming tea.

Gonorrhoea – Also known as the 'Clap.' A nasty sexually transmitted infection, that sees stinky green goo seeping from your schlong, fanny, mouth or rectum.

Hairy onions – Also Wesley Warren's domain.

Helmet – Condom.

Hypothermia – The state of being so cold your body's organs begin to shut down. Common in old people who can't afford electricity in the winter.

Intern – A jumped up little doctor wannabe. Not quite there yet!

Member – A penis. Not to be confused with a 'member' of parliament, although there are many members of parliament who are complete dicks.

Mothers little helpers – *Valium* or calm the fuck down pill.

Narcissist – A nasty fucker who thinks the world revolves around them.

Niagara Falls/Moment – Not to be confused with the beautiful falls themselves, it relates to the Fannies' weak and stretched bladders.

Number Two – Shit, crap , poo , stinker.

Obstetrician – Someone who performs the Fanny finger a lot!

Och aye the noo that is a big 'un – Translates as example of an overt Scotticism: "Oh yes, just now, that is a big one."

Other half – Husband, wife, lover, partner, girlfriend, boyfriend, dog, cat, or in the case of the farm hand, his calf.

Picket Fence – An unfortunate person with protruding teeth.

PC Robot – This refers to one's political correctness. However, a real PC robot is actually a standalone hybrid computer that can perform tasks with its own arms and joints like a human being. One day it may be difficult to tell the difference between the two.

Pick and mix – Sweets and candy.

Pleasure Pipe – Whatever hole you choose to use for your sexual pleasure.

Plumber's Crack – The parting of a person's butt cheeks-usually when a plumber bends over in his dirty jeans.

Pop your clogs – Dead, really dead.

Pubic Flurry – A small, swirling mass of pubic hair, which is moved by a sudden gust of wind, or Dr Weasel's breath.

Psychopath – Unstable fuckers who are as immoral in their antisocial behaviour as they are in their ability to form meaningful relationships with anyone.

Rusty Bullet Hole – Slang name for one's anus horribilus, aka Lord Windy-bottom's potential side-effects from the insertion of the snowflake can.

Sack of Shit – Commonly known as a mind fucking, crazy making narcissist.

Saloon Doors – A slang term for the female 'Labia Majora' or 'vaginal lips.'

Scabby Cow – A cow covered in scabs.

Schlong – A penis, dick or willy. The term 'schlong' has also been used in a poetic sense within this book.

Self-Entitled, Wound-Up Git – An anal-retentive toss pot.

Small/short man syndrome – Technically, it is an inferiority complex, where the person attempts to overcompensate for their perceived shortcoming. A small man, with a big ego.

Sociopath – A person who cannot understand others' feelings. A real mind fuck, sociopaths ooze charisma and charm, but are wankers behind closed doors. They lie and deceive, often using false identities.

Sodding – Don't know- we just liked the word.

Sleazy – Creep, stalker, slime ball, slippery snake, a complete nob head.

Sluice – A great big toilet that you can throw anything into… Literally!

Smear – A derogatory and demeaning examination of the middle wind pipe to scrape off bad cells that have been caused by not wearing a helmet.

Stash – Refers to a pile of something, such as the pills in the first aid kit.

Sweaty nads – One's testicles.

The full quid – Means you're not lying – it's actually true!

Tenor – Piss pad.

Tickle my fancy – Sexual stimulation.

Toxic seed – The ejaculation poison that comes out of a narcissist.

Toss pot – An idiot.

Twat – A complete idiot, or a vulgar term for a woman's fanny.

Wank/Wanker – A pretentious prick who acts or behaves in a manner unbecoming of them. A wanker can also be a male who masturbates a lot, often in public toilets.

Vulcan Technique – While fictional in the Dr Spock sense, it is known as the 'sleeper technique' or 'touch of death' technique (in Karate), where pressure is applied by pinching the flow to the carotid artery. Do not try this at home, as people have popped their clogs.